TERRY PITTS

JUMBO PRINT CROSSWORD BOOK FOR GARDENERS

GRUB STREET · LONDON

Published by Grub Street, The Basement, 10 Chivalry Road,
London SW11 1HT

Copyright © Grub Street 1994
Copyright Crosswords © Terry Pitts Fenby 1994

The right of Terry Pitts Fenby to be identified as the author of this work has been
asserted by him in accordance with the Copyright, Designs and Patents Act 1988.

ISBN 0-948817-95-X

Typesetting by Pearl Graphics, Hemel Hempstead
Printed and bound by Biddles Ltd, Guildford and King's Lynn

AUTHOR'S DEDICATION
For Oliver Paul, the apple of my eye

The kiss of the sun for pardon
The song of the birds for mirth
One is nearer God's heart in a garden
Than anywhere else on earth

Dorothy Frances Gurney

JUMBO CROSSWORD 1

ACROSS

1 Summerhouse with commanding view of the landscape *(6)*

5 Teacher who doesn't know his onions may well produce these, figuratively *(8)*

9 Unwanted garden produce of the litter lout species *(5,3)*

10 Training ground *(6)*

11 Japonica genus *(8)*

12 Outline of the plot *(6)*

13 Acid flavour *(8)*

15 Curious creatures lead charmed lives *(4)*

17 Root or stem, linguistically *(4)*

19 Controversial brush with a harebell *(8)*

20 Overcast *(6)*

21 Paving foundation material *(8)*

22 Resin of the *Liquidambar orientale* tree *(6)*

23 Turned to profitable account *(8)*

24 Healing agents for minor cuts *(8)*

25 Country clothes with Scottish associations *(6)*

DOWN

2 Freshwater alga genus *(8)*

3 Atmospheric forces *(8)*

4 Genus of bushy, spreading, perennial succulents with chunky, triangular leaves and masses of fragrant daisy-like flowers *(9)*

5 Portable plants *(9,6)*

6 Water carriers *(7)*

7 Any of several tropical plants of the genus *Sinningia* (8)

8 Colourless glassy variety of gypsum (8)

14 Aromatic herb much used for flavouring (9)

15 Spring- or autumn-flowering corms (8)

16 Classification (8)

17 Thin transparent layer of frozen water (5,3)

18 Position of greatest difficulty (5,3)

19 Hose connection point (7)

JUMBO CROSSWORD 2

ACROSS

1 Old English lavender species, rich in essential oil for potpourri or perfumed bags *(12)*

7 Complete the task, informally *(3,2)*

8 Forced entry by thieves looking for easy pickings *(5,2)*

11 Kelp of the genus *Laminaria* *(7)*

12 Haughty contempt *(7)*

13 Minerals used as a cathartic *(5)*

14 Cramped quarters in the wilderness *(3,6)*

16 Formed into a single mass or cluster *(9)*

19 Munch noisily *(5)*

21 Leaves having a toothed margin *(7)*

23 Veined foliage *(7)*

24 Optimistic about the damaged tea-rose *(7)*

25 Surpass *(5)*

26 Attacks by parasites *(12)*

DOWN

1 High-ranking butterfly *(7)*

2 Ground squirrels *(7)*

3 Tropical American plum tree *(9)*

4 Fix firmly in the mass *(5)*

5 Abroad *(7)*

6 Common name for the garden plant, *Polemonium caeruleum* *(6,6)*

9 Dull yellowish brown *(5)*

10 Colloquial term for London pride *(4-2-6)*

15 Land preserved from urban development *(5,4)*

17 Taxonomic group *(5)*

18 Insect pupae containing grooves or furrows in which the wings and legs are free *(7)*

19 Bitter orange peel flavours this liqueur *(7)*

20 Consultants, colloquially *(7)*

22 Growing vertically *(5)*

JUMBO CROSSWORD 3

<u>ACROSS</u>

1 Vegetable known as a money-maker *(6)*

5 Common name for the *Primula farinosa*, having clusters of purplish flowers with yellow centres *(5-3)*

9 Gardener with mature experience would qualify as this – if you can't manage the job yourself *(3,5)*

10 Sewage disposal tank *(6)*

11 China's largest cultural centre *(8)*

12 Money down the drains *(6)*

13 Bordering *(8)*

15 Sixth month of the Jewish ecclesiastical year *(4)*

17 Variety of runners *(4)*

19 Plant drug induces pleasurable dreaminess *(8)*

20 Weeding with a long-handled implement *(6)*

21 Managing to survive *(8)*

22 Exercises that may help to relieve backache *(3-3)*

23 Recoiled at the slight movement *(8)*

24 Calmness and tranquillity *(8)*

25 Make certain *(6)*

<u>DOWN</u>

2 Make repairs or adjust mechanical tools for the new season *(8)*

3 Plant completes its life cycle in one year *(2,6)*

4 Building contains hop-drying kilns *(9)*

5 Protected species take refuge in the church *(4,2,3,6)*

6 Takes one's breadth away *(7)*

7 Induce a hypnotic state with a delightful prospect through the garden gate *(8)*

8 Going over the top *(8)*
14 Materials necessary for life and growth *(9)*
15 Stress marks *(8)*
16 Free from restraint *(8)*
17 Salad leaves *(8)*
18 Magnificent splendour *(8)*
19 Just stands there, waiting to be knocked down! *(7)*

JUMBO CROSSWORD 4

<u>ACROSS</u>

1   Fictionally elusive herb *(9)*

8   Figuratively, no problems with England's national emblem *(6,2,5)*

11   Drastic pruning witnessed by the Overseas Press and Media Association *(4)*

12   Dust storm *(5)*

13   Computer list of options *(4)*

16   Nematode worms *(7)*

17   Hide *(7)*

18   Leave your mark on the lovely garden *(7)*

20   Reproductive cell develops into a new form without fertilisation *(7)*

21   Hints from one who is a dab hand in the garden *(4)*

22   Roman goddess of flowers *(5)*

23   State-of-the-arts wheeled cultivator creates a fine tilth for a seedbed *(4)*

26   Below zero is normal for this time of year *(5,2,6)*

27   More familiar name for the prairie turnip, *Psoralea esculenta*, of central North America *(9)*

<u>DOWN</u>

2   Flower power keeps the flag in focus *(4)*

3   Amaranth, cow-parsnip or goosefoot are generally known as this *(7)*

4   Pear Sir? They've been carefully sorted and preserved *(7)*

5   The Greek god of love, visibly moved by a rose *(4)*

6   An excess of *Capsicum frutescens* *(3,4,6)*

7 Trees wave here *(anag. 6,7)*

9 Plant scientists *(9)*

10 Fruit of the service tree *(9)*

14 Boiled oatmeal *(5)*

15 A bit of a fight *(5)*

19 Saltwort genus of the goosefoot family *(7)*

20 Youngsters bitten by the gardening bug all want to be one *(1,6)*

24 Agitate the liquid spray *(4)*

25 Reverse what has been done *(4)*

JUMBO CROSSWORD 5

<u>ACROSS</u>

1 Although passed after adjustment, the tools still need straightening out *(6)*

5 Contrived to change the climates to suit the old man's beard *(8)*

9 Leave a tennis ball in the bird bath during these conditions *(6-2)*

10 Outer membrane of a pollen-grain *(6)*

11 Botanical term for a plant that is woody at the base, although the terminal shoots die back in winter *(3-5)*

12 Creature of habit *(6)*

13 Ornamental piece of quartz *(4,4)*

15 A down-to-earth briefing for the International Society of Aviation Writers *(4)*

17 Terms of reference for the Australian Dried Fruits Association *(4)*

19 Hats allow gardeners to toil in shade *(8)*

20 Unit of distance about three miles *(6)*

21 Narrow-bladed knife *(8)*

22 A sound mole deterrent *(6)*

23 Covered with a coating of rust *(8)*

24 Dealers concealed on the demesnes appear to regard the estates as their own *(8)*

25 Dig up *(6)*

<u>DOWN</u>

2 Distilled common scents *(8)*

3 Thick ground cover *(4,4)*

4 Express confidence in the damn thing *(5,2,2)*

5 Landscape architect who destroyed much of the original gardens of Burghley House, Stamford *(10,5)*

6 Potpourri ingredients combined *(5,2)*

7 Island provides warm and humid conditions *(8)*

8 Popeye's nephew named after a perennial climber *(8)*

14 Illicit liqueur, colloquially *(9)*

15 Slopes *(8)*

16 Soil with a pH value of more than seven *(8)*

17 Show surprise to discover the unusual hostas in *(8)*

18 The avens genus, poetically *(4,4)*

19 Shallow dishes for small indoor plants *(7)*

JUMBO CROSSWORD 6

ACROSS

1 Scottish blackberry preserve *(7,5)*
7 Marten's fur found in the bales *(5)*
8 Turned over a poser while resting quietly *(7)*
11 Respire *(7)*
12 Vegetable dishes *(7)*
13 Fertile desert patch *(5)*
14 Fog thick enough to taste! *(9)*
16 Not quite cricket *(3,3,3)*
19 Welsh breed of dog *(5)*
21 Wells *(7)*
23 Mushroom of the genus *Lepiota* *(7)*
24 Assistance at a difficult time *(7)*
25 Perch for domestic fowls *(5)*
26 Wet and warm in the West Indies *(9,3)*

DOWN

1 Units of dry or liquid measures *(7)*
2 Strawberry tree genus *(7)*
3 Apiarist *(9)*
4 Rather unusual to greet a wading bird *(5)*
5 Rope-making grasses available from the seaport *(7)*
6 Plants for pandas *(6,6)*
9 Inclined to be expensive *(5)*
10 ... and trees slid *(anag. 6,6)*
15 A massif of the Himalayas in Nepal *(9)*
17 Purposeful *(5)*

18 Kenyan National Park *(7)*

19 Fruiting spurs *(7)*

20 East Indian wood of an orange-red colour *(7)*

22 Woody perennial plant, smaller than a tree *(5)*

JUMBO CROSSWORD 7

ACROSS

1   Pruning shears *(9)*

8   Another name for the rayless mayweed (*Matricaria suaveolens*) *(9,4)*

11   Kiln dries hops or malt *(4)*

12   Labour-saving device *(5)*

13   Ground layout proposal *(4)*

16   Sloping ground is inclined to be this at the bottom *(7)*

17   Taking great care *(7)*

18   Smelling unpleasantly *(7)*

20   Trees produce hairy fruits which ripen in autumn, releasing edible, triangular nuts *(7)*

21   Animal excrement, politely *(4)*

22   Gardeners' Question Time *(5)*

23   Information briefing *(4)*

26   Babylonian wonder *(7,6)*

27   Caterpillar associated with Sir Francis Chichester *(5,4)*

DOWN

2   Beautiful garden, sadly overgrown, has a need for attention *(4)*

3   Showing new shoots *(7)*

4   Free-living nematode *(7)*

5   Sowed lines *(4)*

6   Celebration of 24th June *(10,3)*

7   Heavy charge for the weather forecast *(4,2,7)*

9   Plant protector *(4,5)*

10   Blooming *(2,7)*

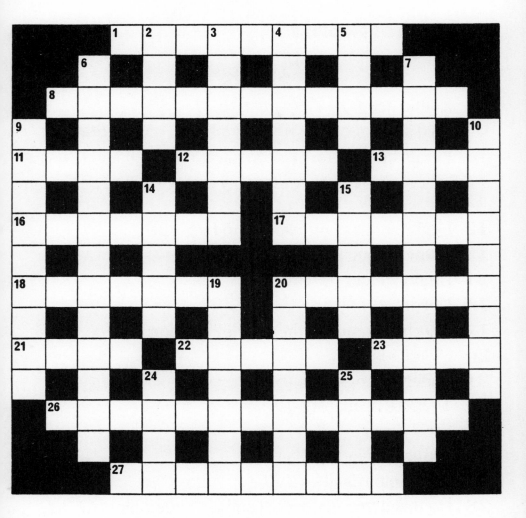

14 If it's not completely genuine – run! *(3,2)*
15 Bury in the soil *(5)*
19 Field of activity *(7)*
20 Common name for the Tasmanian Eucalyptus *(4,3)*
24 Unattractive cross between a tangerine, a grapefruit and a Seville orange *(4)*
25 Fine gravel *(4)*

JUMBO CROSSWORD 8

ACROSS

1 Edible seeds of *Vicia faba* (5,5)

6 Bird language (4)

10 Petals bend to form a compact, round shape (7)

11 Where one might reasonably expect to find a Persian garden (7)

12 Leguminous plant used as fodder (9)

13 Growing out (5)

14 Heavyweight tomato (5)

15 Uproot (9)

17 Another name for the Scarlet Pimpernel (9)

20 Cloudiness (5)

21 Widely recognised (5)

23 Termite predators (9)

25 *See 3 down*

26 Shaggy, unkempt hair (7)

27 Tolerable results (2-2)

28 Do this if you need ideal soil for vegetables (3,3,4)

DOWN

1 Sheer delight (5)

2 Hide in a family of monocotyledons with highly specialised flowers (9)

3 & 25 Across Whose declaration was it that 'one is nearer God's heart in a garden than anywhere else on earth'? (7,7,7)

4 Unpleasant to look at (7)

5 Things to be specially marked or observed (7)

7 Stem sheath (5)

8 Female organs of a flower (9)

9 Noisy, mischievous corvine bird of the genus *Pica* (8,6)

14 People who live (or work) in glasshouses should expect a few of these (9)

16 Not quite freezing (5,4)

18 Informers in the field (7)

19 Raison d'être of forbidden fruits (2,5)

22 *Iris florentina* with a fragrant rootstock (5)

24 Rock plant has white, yellow or pink flowers (5)

JUMBO CROSSWORD 9

ACROSS

1 A cryptogam *(10)*
6 Soil with a pH value of less than seven *(4)*
10 Maytime darlings *(3,4)*
11 Nip across the ruts to see the unusual vegetables *(7)*
12 Top quality *(4,5)*
13 Fully grown insect consumes a friendly Spaniard *(5)*
14 It's developed all wrong, for a change *(5)*
15 Pull up by the roots *(9)*
17 Occupational hazard for fine weather gardeners *(9)*
20 Avaricious palm *(5)*
21 Trembling poplar *(5)*
23 Defines a plant in which the individual flat-topped flower stalks arise from a central point *(9)*
25 Examine carefully *(7)*
26 Warning signal *(7)*
27 Creature comfort *(4)*
28 Gardeners' Question Time team *(10)*

DOWN

1 May drop unless controlled before full maturity *(5)*
2 Uncontrolled vegetation *(9)*
3 Vulnerable stage of development *(5,3,6)*
4 Entangle *(7)*
5 Capsule contains insect eggs *(7)*
7 Translucent earthenware *(5)*
8 Apple variety *(9)*
9 Garden pond *(10,4)*
14 Slow development *(9)*

16 Expressly old-fashioned but not obsolete *(9)*

18 Prickly pear with a secret Utopian existence *(7)*

19 Surround *(7)*

22 A nuisance having damaged steps in the garden *(5)*

24 Landed gentry *(5)*

JUMBO CROSSWORD 10

ACROSS

1 Large fruit of *Ananassa sativa* *(9)*

8 Fruit and vegetables grown for the table *(7,6)*

11 Beneficial garden animal *(4)*

12 French mustard *(5)*

13 Bonsai version *(4)*

16 Gardening broadcast *(7)*

17 Flush *(7)*

18 Colourful time to visit glorious Vermont *(7)*

20 Gentle slope *(7)*

21 Plant supports on site *(4)*

22 Pay out in allotments *(5)*

23 Unusually late, so divided it and went back to the others *(2,2)*

26 *Betula pendula* trees *(6,7)*

27 Characteristic of the Iceberg lettuce *(9)*

DOWN

2 Dead-headed the broom, so she came up to scratch *(4)*

3 Late afternoon *(7)*

4 Homing birds *(7)*

5 Traditional herbal remedies *(4)*

6 Entrenched in a last ditch, colloquially *(3,4,4,2)*

7 Plant sheds its leaves annually *(9,4)*

9 Derivatives from the main stem *(9)*

10 Traditional name for the *Lilium lancifolium* plant *(5,4)*

14 Main branches *(5)*

15 Refuse *(5)*

19 Porters written in as noisy bird scarers *(7)*

20 Blue flowers soaked in neat gin *(7)*

24 Finished *(4)*

25 Only four pips in the pack *(4)*

JUMBO CROSSWORD 11

ACROSS

1 Helpful guides in the hothouse *(12)*

7 Made to drive through the wood *(5)*

8 Sage, ironically *(7)*

11 Cathedral city *(7)*

12 Stunted in growth *(7)*

13 Conspicuous success with a cleat *(5)*

14 Common name for green woodpeckers *(9)*

16 Sweet scent *(9)*

19 Essential oil obtained from damask roses *(5)*

21 The blow that does nobody any good *(3,4)*

23 Glutted *(7)*

24 Earthy material below the layer normally used in cultivation *(7)*

25 Pollutant *(5)*

26 Surface applications of fertiliser *(3,9)*

DOWN

1 Threadlike stem supports the climber *(7)*

2 Slit tie specially woven for the top class *(7)*

3 Deformed *(9)*

4 Fine sprays *(5)*

5 Storm in a teacup *(7)*

6 Ten fish lured by wild thrips *(12)*

9 An addition to the crowd *(5)*

10 Prepared to amputate limbs without anaesthetic *(4,8)*

15 Richly-coloured game birds with an ant's shape *(9)*

17 Fill in *(2,3)*

18 Short, hairlike organ functions as a root in the lower plants *(7)*

19 Neuopterous insect, similar to a damselfly, whose larva traps its prey in a funnel-shaped sand-hole *(7)*

20 Prickly-headed plants of the genus *Dipsacus* whose hooked bracts are used in raising a nap on cloth *(7)*

22 Dig deep *(5)*

JUMBO CROSSWORD 12

ACROSS

1 Foul-smelling gum resin obtained from some species of *Ferula* (10)

6 Woven rushes *(4)*

10 Common name for *Amaranthus retroflexus* (7)

11 Thorny *(7)*

12 Person with this disorder should try the therapeutic benefit of gardening *(9)*

13 Palindromic opinion held as true *(5)*

14 Sun-dried clay mixed with straw fashions a modest abode *(5)*

15 Red and white flower adopted as a badge by Henry VII *(5,4)*

17 Crushed lime acquires a macho quality despite the strongly scented foliage *(9)*

20 Narrow passages between hedges, etc. *(5)*

21 Chewed whilst growing out, then consumed *(5)*

23 Prepare to ambush *(3,2,4)*

25 To anger at the smell of smoke *(7)*

26 Hair nit came out of nowhere *(4,3)*

27 Movable window frame *(4)*

28 The tragacanth and milk-vetch genus *(10)*

DOWN

1 Panes broken by the shaking poplar *(5)*

2 Bean-like fruit of the carob tree *(9)*

3 British summer, facetiously *(3,4,7)*

4 Ditties inspired by the neatest garden *(7)*

5 Neglected *(7)*

7 Arrange nicely *(5)*

8 Without fragrance *(9)*

9 Set in the ground to grow next spring *(6,8)*

14 Genus of the swallow-wort family, silk-weed *(9)*

16 Useless *(2,2,5)*

18 Consequence of handling monkshood without gloves *(7)*

19 One who makes a choice *(7)*

22 Bloodsucking mites of the *Acarina* order *(5)*

24 Edible rootstocks of the genus *Colocasia*, widely cultivated in the Pacific islands *(5)*

JUMBO CROSSWORD 13

ACROSS

1   Botanical name for the foxglove *(9)*

8   Relating to plant cultivation *(13)*

11 Compact arrangement prepared by the Artificial Flower Manufacturers' Association *(4)*

12 Soil *(5)*

13 Aromatic herb in good condition *(4)*

16 Herbaceous plants of the genus *Viola* *(7)*

17 Root vegetable *(7)*

18 Waterfalls *(7)*

20 Divided into classes *(7)*

21 Portions of a felled tree *(4)*

22 Incline *(5)*

23 Pond *(4)*

26 English explorer introduced the potato to Britain *(6,7)*

27 Former Gardeners' Question Time panellist *(4,5)*

DOWN

2   Smallest part *(4)*

3   Annual returns *(7)*

4   Effect of high humidity *(3,4)*

5   Severe pruning carried out by the International Federation of University Women *(4)*

6   'Roses grow on you' was this comedian's catchphrase *(6,7)*

7   Sunshine *(7,6)*

9   The bellflower genus *(9)*

10 Genus of deciduous shrubs and trees carry clusters of white flowers, followed by bladder-like green fruits *(9)*

14 Time recommended by Alfred Noyes to go down to Kew *(5)*

15 I care about Heather *(5)*

19 Enticed by the fragrance *(7)*

20 Hard Swiss cheese flavoured with sweet clover *(7)*

24 Slight movement in the breeze *(4)*

25 Sustain growth *(4)*

JUMBO CROSSWORD 14

ACROSS

1 Small bulbs, used raw in salads *(6,6)*

7 Substance obtained when turpentine is prepared from dead pine wood to make varnish etc. *(5)*

8 Digging out root crops *(7)*

11 Dried fruit of a cultivated form of *Capsicum frutescens*, ground as a condiment *(7)*

12 More soil than usual *(7)*

13 Not as young as you were *(5)*

14 Extract moisture by exposure to air *(9)*

16 The belladonna lily genus *(9)*

19 A stretch of turf *(5)*

21 Soaked to extract flavour *(7)*

23 It's pouring down when they open *(7)*

24 Narrow waterways *(7)*

25 Bird feeder *(5)*

26 Common term for the *Diptera* order of insects *(12)*

DOWN

1 New potatoes prepared for cooking *(7)*

2 Increase in corrosion *(7)*

3 Fine variety of apple *(9)*

4 Garden tools preserved for the winter *(5)*

5 Conflagration *(7)*

6 Planned sequence of growing produce *(4,8)*

9 Spanish island resort *(5)*

10 Improvements from a single point of view *(6,6)*

15 Characterised by a love of beauty *(9)*

17 Solemnly impressive *(5)*

18 Variety of cherry *(7)*
19 Shape the stone roughly *(7)*
20 Well preserved *(7)*
22 Prescribed quantities *(5)*

JUMBO CROSSWORD 15

ACROSS

1 Terrestrial or epiphytic plant having flowers of unusual shapes and beautiful colours *(6)*

5 Botanical name for bear's breeches *(8)*

9 Cabbage variety with a turnip-shaped stem *(8)*

10 Made from the coarse fibres of *Cannabis sativa* *(6)*

11 Genus of usually blue-flowered herbs, abounding chiefly in alpine regions *(8)*

12 Eggs in the hatchback *(6)*

13 Lists of things to be done *(8)*

15 A stab in the back for this protected species *(4)*

17 Sound of a shattered window could be a pain in the neck! *(4)*

19 Stiff simile associated with the genus *Kniphofia* *(2,1,5)*

20 Observation *(6)*

21 Breathing pore in bark *(8)*

22 Low-pitched neigh *(6)*

23 Coffe-growing state in north-east Africa *(8)*

24 Collective noun for soldier ants? *(8)*

25 Crop returns on cultivation *(6)*

DOWN

2 Former tobacco-growing region *(8)*

3 Raised land formations with sloping sides *(8)*

4 Late English rose seen in parts *(5,4)*

5 Discourages pets from fouling lawns, beds and borders *(6,9)*

6 Long narrow stiff leaves of pines *(7)*

7 Genus of plants with three-lobed leaves, once classed as a section of the *Anemone* genus *(8)*

8 Parasol *(8)*

14 Worth doing while the sun shines *(6,3)*

15 Neither a . . . nor a lender be (where garden tools are concerned) *(8)*

16 Treading heavily underfoot *(8)*

17 Coated with a powdery or waxy bloom *(8)*

18 Refreshing breeze *(4,4)*

19 Initial formation *(7)*

JUMBO CROSSWORD 16

ACROSS

1   Yellow organophosphorus insecticide *(9)*

8   Tools to tidy the borders *(5,8)*

11 Open *(4)*

12 Unusual lines of winter pears *(5)*

13 Mythical nymph who, spurned by Narcissus, pined away until only her voice remained *(4)*

16 Fox holes *(7)*

17 Eye shields *(7)*

18 Wears a stoat's coat *(7)*

20 Cut with shears *(7)*

21 Tall plant of the mallow family, *Hibiscus esculentus* *(4)*

22 Terminate prematurely *(5)*

23 Canadian Society of Forest Engineers gets the chop *(4)*

26 Snug as bugs in a rug *(6,7)*

27 Trapped pests *(9)*

DOWN

2   Simple chlorophyll-containing plant *(4)*

3   Terminal parts of stamens in which the pollen matures *(7)*

4   Welcoming cold shower *(7)*

5   Currently On Her Majesty's Service *(4)*

6   Foundation layer of cement, lime, sand and water *(7,6)*

7   Gentle irrigation method *(7,6)*

9   Common name for fruit borne by the *Cucumis melo* plant *(9)*

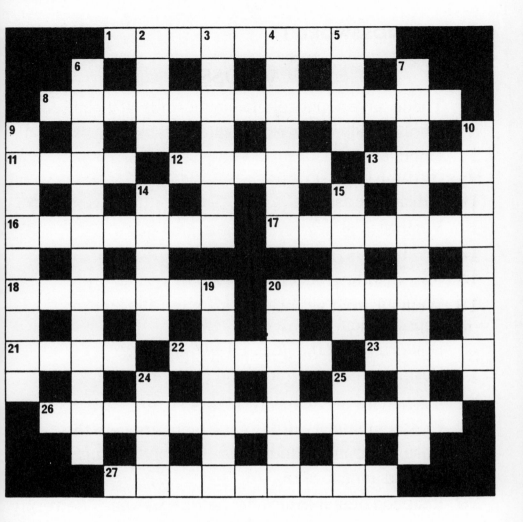

10 Colour in the garden *(4-5)*

14 Hard-wearing trousers, ideal for gardeners *(5)*

15 Repetition brings a pecuniary advantage *(5)*

19 Formal deliberations about a garden seat or bed *(7)*

20 Cuttings specialist *(7)*

24 Short tree branch *(4)*

25 Slight movement *(4)*

JUMBO CROSSWORD 17

ACROSS

1 These have a greater chance of survival if planted outside whilst in flower, than those planted dry in autumn *(5,5)*

6 Netting *(4)*

10 Indicated positions *(7)*

11 Vertical post *(7)*

12 Symbolising *(9)*

13 Sweet variety of cereal grass *(5)*

14 Climbing herb cultivated for forage and soil improvement *(5)*

15 Bowerbirds of the genus *Amblyornis* *(9)*

17 Permits free movement and rotation *(4,5)*

20 Long-shafted clubs used on grass *(5)*

21 Bring to maturity *(5)*

23 Task requiring tremendous effort and strength *(9)*

25 Hoofed animal *(7)*

26 Location of multicellular structure by which flowering plants reproduce *(2,1,4)*

27 Oriental bean sauce *(4)*

28 Place for produce display for the harvest festival *(2,3,5)*

DOWN

1 Scarcely sufficient *(5)*

2 Leaves and flowers developing upwards towards the tip of the plant *(9)*

3 Rules for survival in a hostile environment *(3,2,3,6)*

4 Downfall *(7)*

5 Large vat mixes clay and water *(7)*

7 Steep climb in prospect *(5)*

8 Artificially heated buildings for the cultivation of tender plants *(9)*

9 Dwarf group of beautiful flowers, originally named after the Greek goddess of the rainbow *(4,10)*

14 Plants of the guelder rose and wayfaring tree genus *(9)*

16 Bolting? They're in their element! *(9)*

18 Possess by genetic transmission *(7)*

19 Spoil by exposure to air or moisture *(7)*

22 One of the little people *(5)*

24 Take the drain to the lowest point *(5)*

JUMBO CROSSWORD 18

ACROSS

1 Out of the midday sun *(9)*

8 Multi-purpose compost from the Emerald Isle *(5,4,4)*

11 Narrow beams of light *(4)*

12 Areca nut *(5)*

13 Inspiration *(4)*

16 Despatch *(4,3)*

17 Gardeners' occupational hazard *(7)*

18 Monkey flower genus *(7)*

20 Peaceful *(7)*

21 Aunt gorged on prickly pear *(4)*

22 European owl, *Strix aluco* *(5)*

23 Rose family genus *(4)*

26 Fast-acting source of nitrogen, particularly useful on beetroot and celery *(7,2,4)*

27 Heath family genus *(9)*

DOWN

2 Pond dwellers *(4)*

3 Cooked tree beetle makes a lovely elf meal *(3,4)*

4 Beginning to develop *(7)*

5 Pensioners spray the slippery soap *(4)*

6 I grasp tiny man *(anag. 7,6)*

7 Grounds cleared for pilot tests *(7,6)*

9 Small, night-flying pyralid insect, *Crambus pratellus* *(5,4)*

10 Pepper pods *(9)*

14 Tree or shrub of the genus *Ilex* *(5)*

15 Large orderly pile for storage in the open air *(5)*

19 Broadcast *(7)*
20 Parasite that infects humans *(7)*
24 Cereal grain husks *(4)*
25 Bought or sold second-hand *(4)*

JUMBO CROSSWORD 19

ACROSS

1 Savoury mix produced by a wise old man who used his head *(4,3,5)*

7 Spring flower *(5)*

8 Queen of Fairyland *(7)*

11 Kills pests *(7)*

12 Oak's age has somehow allowed water to percolate *(7)*

13 Sharp prongs set in and forked over *(5)*

14 Fusion of separate growths *(9)*

16 An appreciation of good taste; consider what it teaches! *(9)*

19 Improvised platform *(5)*

21 Surface layer *(7)*

23 Potent alcoholic fruit drink *(7)*

24 West African republic *(7)*

25 Clandestine love affair *(5)*

26 Pleasurable way of life *(8,4)*

DOWN

1 Take the weight off your feet *(3,4)*

2 Rainwater channels *(7)*

3 Upset throws plans into confusion *(5-4)*

4 Arranged appointments *(5)*

5 Fertiliser *(7)*

6 Interconnected underground tunnels used as breeding grounds by leporid mammals *(6,6)*

9 Organisation caters for British military personnel *(5)*

10 Breathtaking *(3-9)*

15 Shaped like a snail's shell *(9)*

17 Jargon *(5)*

18 Commonplace *(7)*

19 Extremely large Californian coniferous tree *(7)*

20 Dig up *(7)*

22 New Zealand tree *Myoporum laetum*, with narrow leaves and small white purple-spotted flowers *(5)*

JUMBO CROSSWORD 20

ACROSS

1 Essential tool for a gardener on his knees *(6)*
5 Hanging beds *(8)*
9 Aboriginal name for the Australian eucalyptus tree *(8)*
10 Flower decorations *(6)*
11 System of holding land in absolute ownership *(8)*
12 Dried grape *(6)*
13 Canadian salad dressing based on mayonnaise, chopped gherkins, etc., — Island *(8)*
15 Various purposes of employ *(4)*
17 Red star on the blink *(4)*
19 A quick simile *(2,1,5)*
20 Tea-set laid out in the grounds for a change *(6)*
21 Tied label *(5,3)*
22 Common name for a diving bird of the genus *Cinclus aquaticus (6)*
23 Linked daisies *(2,1,5)*
24 Moving the heavy roller *(8)*
25 Sour-juice plants of the genus *Oxalis (6)*

DOWN

2 Belonging nowhere *(8)*
3 It was old, evidently, when gently stirred *(4,4)*
4 Slippery surface *(9)*
5 Hazel catkins are commonly regarded as such *(7,2,6)*
6 Wild duck, commonplace in the northern hemisphere *(7)*
7 Horned viper genus *(8)*

8 Could reduce noise pollution if fitted to lawnmowers! *(8)*

14 Unwelcome creatures on carefully prepared seedbeds *(2,7)*

15 Lawn tennis court not yet ready for the players *(8)*

16 Another name for the groundnut *(5,3)*

17 Separates grain or seeds from wheat *(8)*

18 Salts turn red litmus paper blue *(8)*

19 Fish food *(4,3)*

JUMBO CROSSWORD 21

ACROSS

1 Gardening columnist shares his name with a village near Kettering, Northamptonshire *(10)*

6 Enlarged, fleshy, bulb-like base of a stem *(4)*

10 Brought to maturity *(7)*

11 Genus of annual onagraceous plants, native of North America, synonymous with *Godetia* *(7)*

12 A pentose sugar derived from plant gums *(9)*

13 Grease strips protect fruit trees from winter moth caterpillars *(5)*

14 *Hedera canariensis* does this so well, no wonder it's on film! *(5)*

15 Destroy micro-organisms *(9)*

17 Outdated weapons make useful choppers *(9)*

20 Artificial union obtained through hard work *(5)*

21 Molehill *(5)*

23 Plants produced by human skill *(9)*

25 Everlasting *(7)*

26 Common term for *Nepeta* *(7)*

27 Divots *(4)*

28 A gardener's place of rest? *(3,2,5)*

DOWN

1 Earth *(5)*

2 Fanciful landscape artist *(9)*

3 Terraced layout *(7,7)*

4 Strenuous work *(7)*

5 Just half a second to hide the EC trees *(7)*

7 Made of hard, durable wood *(5)*

8 Early common name for the *Spiraea ulmaria* (4-5)

9 Frothy climbing rose, inspired by a meandering sermon, perhaps (8,6)

14 Creeping plant cultivated in many forms for these edible cylindrical fruits (9)

16 18th-century follies seen as manifestations of vacuous mentalities (9)

18 Sour orange (7)

19 Hot, oppressive wind (7)

22 Alter drastically (5)

24 Garden designs should exploit the natural characteristics of these (5)

JUMBO CROSSWORD 22

ACROSS

1   Lettuce variety *(6,3)*

8   Thoughtful observation *(13)*

11   Safety measure *(4)*

12   Reproductive structure in a mushroom stalk evolved there out of spite *(5)*

13   Parasitic mite of the family *Sarcoptidae* *(4)*

16   Selected one of several small wooded dells, for special treatment *(7)*

17   Cry out with excitement *(7)*

18   Winter wind plays havoc with the ramtils, the seeds of which are used as a source of oil *(7)*

20   Nutritive stage in the food chain *(7)*

21   Horticultural display *(4)*

22   Aromatic seeds used for flavouring and as a condiment *(5)*

23   Foreign type, inclined to lean a bit *(4)*

26   Seasoned or hardened by exposure *(7-6)*

27   Brittle food containers applied as a slug repellent *(9)*

DOWN

2   A very small amount *(4)*

3   Scrumpers' desire *(7)*

4   Sounds of hedge trimming proceeding from the shadows *(7)*

5   Gardener's snack nibbled on the chair *(4)*

6   Rock movements *(7,6)*

7   Another name for prickly ash *(9,4)*

9 Popular name for the edible red seaweed, also known as carrageen *(5,4)*

10 Abhorred by organic gardeners *(9)*

14 Outdoor lighting *(5)*

15 Cutting prepared for grafting *(5)*

19 Evergreen shrubs to rest on, with a sense of achievement *(7)*

20 Useful, perhaps, for one who finds the needle in a haystack *(7)*

24 Beetle of the family *Lucanidae* *(4)*

25 Autumn in Vermont *(4)*

JUMBO CROSSWORD 23

ACROSS

1 Important aspect of the landscaped garden *(10)*

6 Jack Horner's fruit *(4)*

10 Fever characterised by a strawberry tongue *(7)*

11 Cleared away roots, stumps, etc. *(7)*

12 Poses an identity problem *(9)*

13 Plant yielding curare *(5)*

14 Sounds too cold to be a hot dry wind *(5)*

15 Large area *(9)*

17 Verge clod turned over by a border collie, perhaps *(6,3)*

20 Zodiacal character study should surely benefit growers .... *(5)*

21 Mouse-like insectivorous mammal *(5)*

23 Torn sapling leaves a round gash *(6,3)*

25 Canadian province *(7)*

26 Areas of high humidity *(7)*

27 Poison within an otherwise nutritious pulse seed *(4)*

28 Deadly nightshade *(10)*

DOWN

1 Culinary herb *(5)*

2 Herbal tea *(9)*

3 Rust-proofed fencing material *(10,4)*

4 Larger than average *(7)*

5 Lack of attention *(7)*

7 Unearthly balance *(5)*

8 Conditions at the bottom of the pond *(9)*

9 Fertiliser helps grass recover from summer stress and protects against winter weather *(6,4,4)*

14 Amaranthaceous garden or pot plant, *Celosia cristata*, has feathery plume-like flowers *(9)*

16 Reproduction *(9)*

18 Wild prickly plant should perhaps be kept on a leash? *(3,4)*

19 Got tall with poor articulation *(7)*

22 Climbing palm of the genus *Calamus* *(5)*

24 Genus of decorative perennial herbaceous plants from Asia, with ribbed basal leaves and blue, white and lilac flowers *(5)*

JUMBO CROSSWORD 24

ACROSS

1 Members of the Geraniaceae family *(12)*
7 Languid tulip may have drunk too much *(3,2)*
8 Take care *(4,3)*
11 Asp with a broken tail turned up out of thin air *(7)*
12 Condition *(7)*
13 Wild chrysanthemum *(5)*
14 Altitude above ground level *(9)*
16 Sensitive probe *(9)*
19 Indigestible mixture of hedge and tree clippings *(5)*
21 Clothes line *(7)*
23 Forced to the stage of simulated conversation *(7)*
24 Beverages made from the sap of palm trees *(7)*
25 It's nuder below the surface *(5)*
26 Dunnock *(5,7)*

DOWN

1 Shield-shaped leaf *(7)*
2 Geometrical character of the ouvirandra leaf, *Aponogeton fenestrale*, a Madagascan water plant *(7)*
3 Spray drives away insects *(9)*
4 Common name for a species of primrose, *Primula elatior*, with pale yellow flowers *(5)*
5 Genus of the morning-glory family containing many species with ornamental flowers *(7)*
6 Pulpy berry of the genus *Passiflora* *(12)*
9 Small tan-coloured antelope of East Africa has spike-like horns *(5)*
10 What a bird in the hand is worth *(3,2,3,4)*

15 Smell of burned vegetables *(9)*

17 Aquatic larva of the dragonfly *(5)*

18 Nature's forces wearing away the earth's surface *(7)*

19 Rock of ages *(7)*

20 Indispensable garden tool gets the push *(1,6)*

22 … and mellow fruitfulness *(5)*

JUMBO CROSSWORD 25

ACROSS

1 Parasitic fungus capable of killing whole trees *(5,4)*

8 Granadilla *(13)*

11 Bird of prey on offer? *(4)*

12 Personal record *(5)*

13 Counsellor is not down to earth *(4)*

16 Meshed fabric *(7)*

17 Necessary *(7)*

18 Fruitless, going round in these *(7)*

20 Dead rotten throughout *(7)*

21 Shaft *(4)*

22 Impure form of quartz used as a gemstone *(5)*

23 Married German woman *(4)*

26 Hints on growing these succulent shoots *(9,4)*

27 Vegetable association with glazed translucent paper *(5,4)*

DOWN

2 Force it out *(4)*

3 Making amends and not gain *(7)*

4 Dried stigmas of the genus *Crocus sativus* to flavour or colour food *(7)*

5 Produces musical sounds on the wind *(4)*

6 Enjoy the flavour with spices *(3,4,6)*

7 Insectivorous plant with hinged leaves *(5,8)*

9 Kaolin *(5,4)*

10 Removed right down to the roots *(6,3)*

14 Open tract of uncultivated land *(5)*

15 Fight over the garden boundary *(5)*

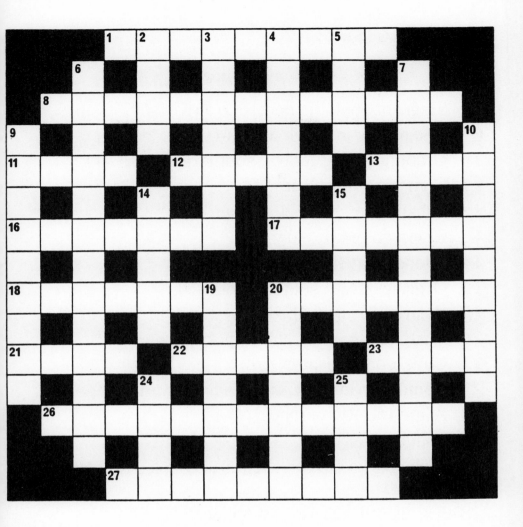

19 Edible fruit-bearing cactus *(7)*

20 Deviations from the chosen path *(7)*

24 Wave the wand for a new day *(4)*

25 Contractual arrangement agreed with the Royal Town
Planning Institute *(4)*

JUMBO CROSSWORD 26

ACROSS

1   Stagnant pools connected to a river *(10)*
6   Bog myrtle in a high wind *(4)*
10 Grape-growing centre, southern France *(7)*
11 Comparatively close *(7)*
12 Subshrub of genus *Artimisia* *(9)*
13 Environment friendly *(5)*
14 A kind of lavender *(5)*
15 Organic oils present in plants *(9)*
17 Related species *(4,5)*
20 Waited for a favourable opportunity *(5)*
21 Covered with water *(5)*
23 Common name for *Aconitum lycoctonum* *(9)*
25 A late variety, perhaps? *(7)*
26 Sought after *(7)*
27 Builder who offered shelter to couples caught in the rain *(4)*
28 Excellent progress to begin with *(5,5)*

DOWN

1   Determines the pecking order *(5)*
2   Resists decomposition *(9)*
3   Reduces air current velocity to a ghost of a breeze *(9,5)*
4   Religious clipping *(7)*
5   Stock farms *(7)*
7   White poplar tree *(5)*
8   Gentle Dan totally confused by the angled net *(9)*
9   Flower display suspended *(7,7)*

14 Chief centre of central northern Saskatchewan, the great world producer of hard wheat *(9)*

16 Refreshing infusion *(6,3)*

18 Time to make a fresh start *(3,4)*

19 The long, dry, dehiscent fruit of cruciferous plants such as the wallflower *(7)*

22 Betel-nut genus of palms *(5)*

24 If you can't mend it, chop the top off! *(3,2)*

JUMBO CROSSWORD 27

<u>ACROSS</u>

1   Common name for the widely cultivated *Allium sativum* plant *(6)*

5   Heart stimulant obtained from its soft wrinkled leaves *(8)*

9   Driver carried around landscaped grounds *(4,4)*

10   Wasps' nest is a potential . . . *(6)*

11   Special way of talking to plants? *(8)*

12   Burrowing wasp *(6)*

13   Oppressively close atmosphere *(8)*

15   Case full of separate, single pips *(4)*

17   Boys will be boys – unless one turns out to be a spring onion! *(4)*

19   Rubiaceous plant of the genus *Galium* has small white or yellow flowers and hairy fruits *(8)*

20   American Judas tree *(6)*

21   One pea is quite a change from these ranunculaceous shrubs *(8)*

22   Not dense *(6)*

23   Another name for frankincense *(8)*

24   At home on occasions *(4,4)*

25   Short periods of changeable weather *(6)*

<u>DOWN</u>

2   Fragrant, sweet-scented and spicy *(8)*

3   Dead *(8)*

4   Common name for *Chelidonium majus*, supposed to flower when the swallows came, and to perish when they went *(9)*

5   Artificial ponds *(10,5)*

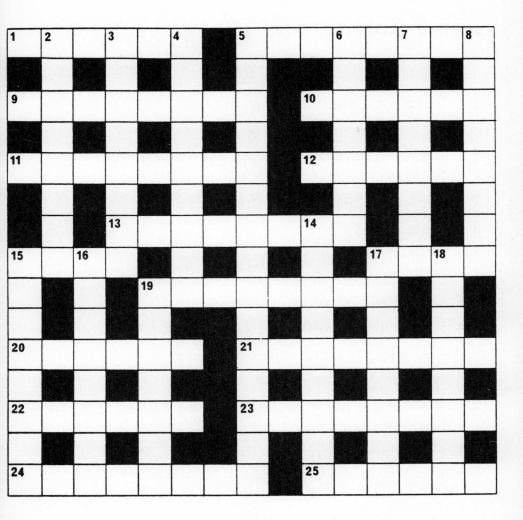

6   Setting greenhouse windows *(7)*

7   Anthropoid ape, *Pongo pygmaeus*, seen entering the citrus house *(8)*

8   Open a strange deal door to find the golden land *(8)*

14   Establishments for commericial growers *(9)*

15   Out of doors *(8)*

16   Emit light, heat, etc. *(8)*

17   Pastoral ballet *(4,4)*

18   Hermaphroditic *(8)*

19   Discoloured fruit due to superficial injury *(7)*

<u>ACROSS</u>

1   Time for an autumn lawn dressing *(9)*

8   Land moss bloom *(anag. 6,7)*

11 Plant parasite on the short list – and about time too! *(4)*

12 Electrical palindrome *(5)*

13 New growth *(4)*

16 Frozen drippings *(7)*

17 Small in circumference in proportion to height *(7)*

18 Closer together *(7)*

20 Somewhere in the field *(4-3)*

21 Tall stiff marsh or water grass *(4)*

22 Ignition of burning bush vapour *(5)*

23 Rounded protuberance projects upwards from the roots of the swamp cypress *(4)*

26 Bright and vigorous, colloquially *(5,2,1,5)*

27 *Vaccinium macrocarpum* fruit sauce *(9)*

<u>DOWN</u>

2   Picked a bone over the *Diospyros* tree *(4)*

3   Being outside just for a change is boring *(7)*

4   Any plant of the genus *Malva*   *(7)*

5   Tranquil rest *(4)*

6   Common name for the hardy genus of perennials *Dicentra spectabilis* *(8,5)*

7   No light matter if it inhibits natural growth *(5,8)*

9   Bonsai style *(9)*

10 Genus of shrubby plants with large globular clusters of showy flowers; natives of Japan *(9)*

14 Grown excess quantities *(5)*
15 Dry or sandy soil *(5)*
19 Hold back *(7)*
20 Large measure of land *(7)*
24 Drug addict, colloquially *(4)*
25 Alike as two peas *(4)*

JUMBO CROSSWORD 29

ACROSS

1 Astringent medicinal solution contains an extract of the bark and leaves of *Hamamelis virginiana* *(5,5)*

6 Manor house, colloquially *(4)*

10 Side shoot *(7)*

11 Cuts above the rest *(7)*

12 Drains the cess pool *(4,5)*

13 Ripened ovary of a flowering plant *(5)*

14 Damage irreparably *(5)*

15 Pressurised liquid contains carbon dioxide *(4,5)*

17 Showing through *(9)*

20 Fencing equipment *(5)*

21 Cutting tool *(5)*

23 Riddle *(9)*

25 Not really established here now, but transplanting could finish it off *(7)*

26 Ambitious scheme conceived during a break in the dig *(3,4)*

27 Earthy language from the grass roots *(4)*

28 A forest in springtime *(5,5)*

DOWN

1 Water taps *(5)*

2 Carved tribal symbol is a temple, too *(5,4)*

3 National Trust parkland with pergola, rhododendrons and azaleas, near Macclesfield *(4,4,6)*

4 Earth features preserved as slate *(7)*

5 Private area revealed *(7)*

7 French leaves *(5)*

8 Strong ties *(9)*

9 Commemorative entertainment out of doors *(3,6,5)*

14 Young plants developing after germination *(9)*

16 Formal Japanese garden would be incomplete without it *(3,6)*

18 Such a small beginning is somehow unclear *(7)*

19 Raise to a higher level *(7)*

22 Cut off with the teeth *(5)*

24 Periodic feeding *(5)*

JUMBO CROSSWORD 30

ACROSS

1 The sweet green fruit of this West Indian evergreen tree is a powerful contraceptive *(6)*

5 Tiny gardens *(8)*

9 If you find one of its bones, it could be a plant! *(8)*

10 Pyramid selling probably inspired here by the little beggars *(2,4)*

11 Convert common names to the universal language of botany *(8)*

12 Earthenware vegetable dish *(6)*

13 Annuals and perennials with poppy-like flowers that are good for cutting *(8)*

15 Quiet retreat *(4)*

17 ... of the earth; the finest of their kind *(4)*

19 Sea trees hydrolised into alcohols and acids *(8)*

20 Superficially attractive *(6)*

21 Spider-threads *(8)*

22 Marijuana cigarette, colloquially *(6)*

23 Appearing once a year *(8)*

24 Harvested *(8)*

25 Growing old *(6)*

DOWN

2 Bird-life found in a region *(8)*

3 Fine sprayer *(8)*

4 Disease due to infestation by mites *(9)*

5 Kent, colloquially *(6,2,7)*

6 Beautiful trees, some yielding valuable furniture wood *(7)*

7 Evergreen, epiphytic orchid for a cool greenhouse *(8)*

8   Still waters capable of producing gnats *(8)*

14 The baobab genus *(9)*

15 Bound to advance in the spring *(8)*

16 Curiously, these novelty tin trees can make
    money! *(8)*

17 Keep them apart: pears and tea don't mix *(8)*

18 Yellow pigment obtained from dyer's weed *(8)*

19 Highest degree *(7)*

JUMBO CROSSWORD 31

ACROSS

1 A plant of the spurge and poinsettia genus *(9)*

8 Tropical American genus, its triplets of flowers almost concealed by rosy or purple bracts *(13)*

11 Garden seat faces the morning sun *(4)*

12 Remove fine growths *(5)*

13 Take care over this maple genus *(4)*

16 Stout shoes entirely consumed by a rose-bug attack *(7)*

17 Backache *(7)*

18 Salad plants of the chicory genus *(7)*

20 Left over *(7)*

21 Stalk of a moss capsule *(4)*

22 Sabre buried in the Scottish hills *(5)*

23 New Zealand shrubs of the genus *Coriaria*, having poisonous black berries *(4)*

26 Preparations for the main crop of potatoes *(2,3,8)*

27 Marketable produce *(4,5)*

DOWN

2 Advocate persistently *(4)*

3 Hilltops *(7)*

4 Recovery from neglect *(7)*

5 Misfortunes *(4)*

6 Decorative material from Gloucestershire for the ultimate rock garden *(8,5)*

7 Tranquillity *(5,3,5)*

9 Arrested bird identified in the line-up *(9)*

10 Botanic garden of trees *(9)*

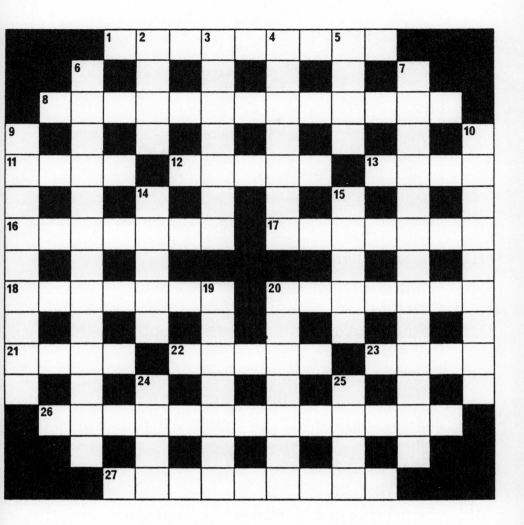

14 Tropical American tree of the genus *Psidium*; its yellow, pear-shaped fruit often made into jelly *(5)*

15 Mashed potatoes *(5)*

19 Relieve an itch *(7)*

20 Ruminant mammal of the family *Cervidae (3,4)*

24 Tea plant raised on heat *(4)*

25 Briefing accepted by the International Committee for Bird Protection *(4)*

JUMBO CROSSWORD 32

ACROSS

1   Organic fertiliser, rich in nitrogen and ideal for growing leaf crops *(5,5)*

6   Contractual arrangement creates a shortage for the British Farm Produce Council *(4)*

10 Strolling gently around the balm *(7)*

11 Ominous sounds suggest an early end to work in the garden *(7)*

12 Stretched *(9)*

13 Hindu god governs the weather and dispenses rain *(5)*

14 Young woman on the line has evidently caught the silly fool *(5)*

15 Reproduced the original concept *(9)*

17 Botanical name for the Canterbury bell *(9)*

20 Natural characteristic of the tribe that turned on the hand that feeds it *(5)*

21 Top of the family tree? *(5)*

23 Softly rustling *(9)*

25 Chemical obtained from lichens and from which the dyes found in litmus were derived *(7)*

26 Simplicity *(7)*

27 Darker part of twilight *(4)*

28 Devotee *(10)*

DOWN

1   Deadly nightshade *(5)*

2   Flower show *(2,7)*

3   Last message from a wilting plant *(5,3,1,5)*

4   Indicates insufficient water for the potted plant *(7)*

5   A group of eight *(7)*

7   Past its blooming best *(5)*

8 Umbelliferous plant whose leaves and seeds are used as a food flavouring *(9)*

9 Cones used in making gin *(7, 7)*

14 Compound plant consists of a fungus and an alga living symbiotically *(9)*

16 Mexican foxglove genus *(9)*

18 Torn slip found in the twentieth letter from Greece *(7)*

19 Potent green alcoholic drink containing wormwood could make the heart grow fonder, perhaps? *(7)*

22 Nettle sting remedy *(5)*

24 Don't be a stick in the mud – experiment! *(3,2)*

JUMBO CROSSWORD 33

ACROSS

1   Common name for *Verbascum thapsus* *(6,3)*
8   Chelsea Flower Show grounds *(5,8)*
11 Seedy area *(4)*
12 Sun-baked earth *(5)*
13 Avens genus *(4)*
16 *Bignonia capreolata* flower opens with an ostentatious flourish *(7)*
17 Aspen-like tremble *(7)*
18 Predators *(7)*
20 Pot boiler *(7)*
21 Flower used figuratively as a thing of purity and whiteness *(4)*
22 Slender, thread-like root could also be brief *(5)*
23 Scottish fencers' union for non-professionals *(4)*
26 Weeding posture *(2,6,5)*
27 Mushroom, colloquially *(4,5)*

DOWN

2   The first gardener *(4)*
3   Variety of sweet cherry *(7)*
4   Family members *(7)*
5   Columbus is the capital of this US state *(4)*
6   Category for any growth requiring an optimum temperature range over 24°C *(8,5)*
7   Travel near dew to locate this perfume *(8,5)*
9   Bloodsucking insect causes sleeping sickness *(6,3)*
10 Latin name for love-lies-bleeding *(9)*
14 Sap sucker *(5)*

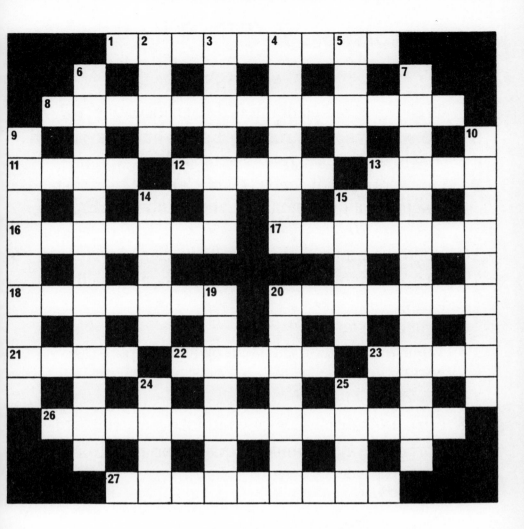

15 Characteristic feature of kale *(5)*

19 Tall, slender and frail *(7)*

20 Successfully treated a dire cut *(5,2)*

24 Abominable snowman *(4)*

25 Short term for the Irish National Teachers' Organisation *(4)*

JUMBO CROSSWORD 34

<u>ACROSS</u>

1 Orange-rooted plant offered as an incentive *(6)*

5 Spiny rutaceous citrus tree bears sour pear-shaped fruit yielding a fragrant essential oil *(8)*

9 Genus of papilionaceous plants, among the most magnificent ornamental climbers known in English gardens *(8)*

10 Burrowing animal noted for its black and white cap *(6)*

11 Gentle bird of a feather violated when it couldn't fit in, perhaps? *(8)*

12 Sensitive plant *(6)*

13 Vehicle parked on the lawn by an irresponsible person *(8)*

15 Goddess of fertility *(4)*

17 Cereals associated with youthful promiscuity *(4)*

19 Forget-me-nots would be inappropriate for one diagnosed as such *(8)*

20 Riddle *(6)*

21 Comic verse *(8)*

22 Atmospheric disturbances *(6)*

23 Natural elements *(8)*

24 Applied fertiliser *(8)*

25 Following the scent *(6)*

<u>DOWN</u>

2 Unusual method of cell division *(8)*

3 Secluded places for quiet meditation *(8)*

4 Enclosure for small land animals *(9)*

5 Best cooking apple *(7,8)*

6 Stone from Tangier *(7)*

7 Fragrant flowers detected with a long aim *(8)*

8 Paved areas serve partly as gardens *(8)*

14 Inclination of one faced with an overgrown jungle *(5,4)*

15 Simmered under water *(8)*

16 Provide artificial streams to promote vegetation *(8)*

17 Natural earth mixtures used as pigments *(8)*

18 Cyatheaceae family, in need of a change, accommodated rent-free *(4,4)*

19 Hidden hollows *(7)*

JUMBO CROSSWORD 35

ACROSS

1 Fast-growing deciduous spreading plant gives off oven-free heat after treatment *(4,2,6)*

7 Cooked a rice mixure on waste ground *(5)*

8 Place *(7)*

11 Reconstituted gelatin lifts the spirits *(7)*

12 Hairy ridge *(7)*

13 Three goddesses of destiny make a feast of it *(5)*

14 Genus of western wheatgrass which grows well in very dry areas *(9)*

16 Give an inadequate supply of nutrients *(9)*

19 Scarf *(5)*

21 Make slightly damp *(7)*

23 Flower receptacle encloses and fuses with the reproductive organs *(7)*

24 Australian parrot of the genus *Platycercus elegans* *(7)*

25 Rock plant of the Saxifraga genus, pink flushed with a sense of its superior character in London *(5)*

26 Flower display with the subtle mark of Cupid *(1,4,2,5)*

DOWN

1 & 6 Left blooming alone (Thomas Moore, 1779-1852) *(3,4,4,2,6)*

2 Alchemical preparations supposed to be capable of prolonging life *(7)*

3 Citrus-flavoured drink *(9)*

4 Made with a rush *(5)*

5 Discovered a new part of Belgium *(7)*

9 Ventilator *(5)*

10 English architect noted for his creative partnership with Gertrude Jekyll *(5, 7)*

15 Fruit of the *Capsicum frutescens* plant *(3,6)*

17 Feeds drop by drop *(5)*

18 Sounds made by the seed capsules of *Pedicularis palustris* *(7)*

19 Diminutive folk at the bottom of the garden *(7)*

20 Area of the facial wall of an insect's head, between the labrum and the frons *(7)*

22 Small New Zealand tree yields useful timber *(5)*

JUMBO CROSSWORD 36

ACROSS

1 Aves community *(4,6)*

6 Home-made insecticide *(4)*

10 Peculiar to the locality *(7)*

11 Clover-like plant produces racemes of white or yellow flowers with a subtle hint of lime *(7)*

12 Environment *(9)*

13 Jungle country *(5)*

14 Vegetarians' celebration *(5)*

15 Animal feeds on dead organic matter *(9)*

17 A green tit, rather out of sorts, until it pulls itself together *(9)*

20 Fragrant resin found over a mile *(5)*

21 Animal trail *(5)*

23 Perennial nice verse *(4,5)*

25 Gusher *(7)*

26 Fruits of the West Indian sapotaceous tree, *Chrysophyllum cainito*, when cut across, are shaped like this *(2,5)*

27 Observe with a bit of extra-sensory perception *(4)*

28 Common name for the labiate garden plant genus *Dracocephalum*, so-called from the shape of the corolla *(10)*

DOWN

1 Red roots of the goosefoot family *(5)*

2 Songbird related to the thrushes *(9)*

3 Ordinary, colloquially *(6-2-6)*

4 Rose campion genus *(7)*

5 South African genus of the figwort family *(7)*

7 Man-made fibre *(5)*

8 Dried petal mixture with spices *(9)*

9 Maryland's state flower *(5-4,5)*

14 Common yellow butterfly *(9)*

16 Cultivated variety of plum tree, with environmental approval *(9)*

18 Ring of colours *(7)*

19 Dusk *(7)*

22 Species of primrose *(5)*

24 Moved with great care *(5)*

JUMBO CROSSWORD 37

ACROSS

1 North American plant of the lily family has a sweet, edible bulb *(6)*

5 Sword lilies *(8)*

9 Small species of club-rush *(4-4)*

10 Mushroom of the genus *Coprinus* *(6)*

11 Neglected garden tool *(5,3)*

12 Deciduous genus of *Rhododendron* with five stamens and annual leaves *(6)*

13 Fertiliser *(8)*

15 What the nightingale did in Berkeley Square *(4)*

17 Potato seed-buds *(4)*

19 Spicy bark of a lauraceous tree of Sri Lanka *(8)*

20 Soil *(6)*

21 Solid inorganic substances *(8)*

22 Carbohydrate obtained from dahlia roots *(6)*

23 Deficiency of the trace element molybdenum is the likely cause of this problem with brassicas *(2,6)*

24 Abhorred by insects (and small boys) *(8)*

25 Pakistan city *(6)*

DOWN

2 Commercial centre of southern Peru *(8)*

3 Botanical term for mud plant roots that rise erect as breathing organs *(8)*

4 Marrow variety may be stored for several months *(9)*

5 Decorative bric-a-brac could be a strange Roman den *(6,9)*

6 Term for a wild plant that keeps its footing in a place to which it is not native *(7)*

7 The study of new growths *(8)*

8 Graftings *(8)*

14 Produced in a Swiss cheese plant – naturally! *(9)*

15 Hymenopterous insects of the family *Tenthredinidae* *(8)*

16 Cloudiness *(8)*

17 Intrude beyond the boundaries *(8)*

18 Rival seems to be using our metal *(8)*

19 They would not be out of place in a monastery garden *(7)*

JUMBO CROSSWORD 38

ACROSS

1 & 28 Christmas rose genus *(10,10)*

6 Dried ripe female flowers used in brewing *(4)*

10 Walking stick made from the ratan palm *(7)*

11 Cultivated crops *(7)*

12 Watercourse *(9)*

13 Seedless fruit with concealed whiskers *(5)*

14 Weed-free area *(5)*

15 Toadstools come into this category *(3-6)*

17 Soaking *(9)*

20 Praise highly *(5)*

21 Cooked potato of a sort *(5)*

23 Type of bean poles for heavy croppers *(5,4)*

25 Seems unfair to distribute unseasoned softwood timber *(3,4)*

26 Pot-bellied *(7)*

27 Neat smoking pile *(4)*

DOWN

1 Damp weather *(5)*

2 Natural order of bulbous plants bearing large showy flowers atop tall slender stems *(9)*

3 Deviations from the norm *(14)*

4 Rooting support *(7)*

5 Indefinitely large number, colloquially *(7)*

7 Small body in seed-bearing plants develops into the seed after fertilisation *(5)*

8 Species of *Veronica* genus *(9)*

9 Stolen apples *(9,5)*

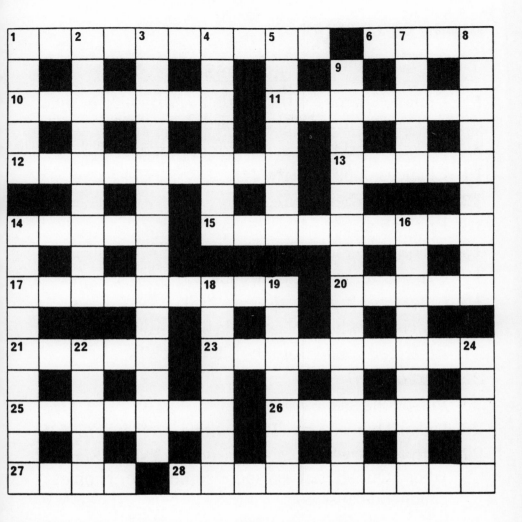

14 Old World coniferous plant of the Pinaceae family *(5,4)*

16 Drug or pesticide made from parts of a plant *(9)*

18 Cut off *(7)*

19 Momentary view contrived by a medium *(7)*

22 Controlled water supply for just one bird? *(5)*

24 Asian bean plants? Just turn them and say so *(5)*

JUMBO CROSSWORD 39

ACROSS

1 Common name for the genus *Stellaria media,* much relished by fowls and cagebirds *(9)*

8 Second World War slogan for gardeners *(3,3,7)*

11 Chances of probability *(4)*

12 Spring into being *(5)*

13 Running water *(4)*

16 Quiet place for meditation *(7)*

17 Ornament for the clothes line *(7)*

18 Celery not fully developed *(2,5)*

20 Species newly established in bare ground *(7)*

21 Reflected sound from the hills *(4)*

22 Turf out *(5)*

23 Poisonous snakes *(4)*

26 Dylan Thomas play (1954) with a latex link *(5,4,4)*

27 18th-century landscaped garden at Esher, Surrey where Queen Victoria spent some of her happiest childhood days *(9)*

DOWN

2 Winged leaf stalk *(4)*

3 Condimental herb bears aromatic seedlike fruit *(7)*

4 Handy dodge around the furrow *(7)*

5 Briefing for the European Free Trade Association *(4)*

6 Not to be thrown away for a poor chance of something better *(4,2,3,4)*

7 A *Clematis* to gladden the eye of passing salesmen *(10,3)*

9 Standardised potting composts *(4,5)*

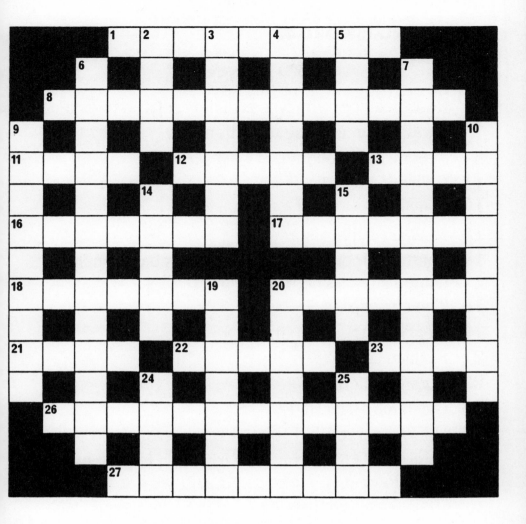

10 Common polyonaceous weed with nodes in its stems *(9)*

14 Take it easy *(5)*

15 Tool removes stubble *(5)*

19 Lightweight clipper *(7)*

20 A hard nut to crack *(7)*

24 Give an account of the legendary bowman who shot at the apple of his eye *(4)*

25 *Linnaea* flower could be one of a pair *(4)*

JUMBO CROSSWORD 40

ACROSS

1   Rose grower, who was probably related to Ena *(4,8)*

7   Shows promising development *(5)*

8   Separating into lots *(7)*

11   Cold climate *(7)*

12   Increasing signs of neglect *(7)*

13   Nursery supervisor *(5)*

14   Southern Indian member of the dogbane family, named after its hard white wood *(5-4)*

16   The cowslip *(4,5)*

19   Deal with the infestation *(5)*

21   Surface layers *(7)*

23   Gigantic cactus *(7)*

24   Gardening hazard *(7)*

25   Uncivilised route through France *(5)*

26   Neglected garden must be irritating for one inclined to lie down on the job ... *(3,2,7)*

DOWN

1   Hooded pigeon *(7)*

2   Boraginaceous plant of the genus *Symphytum* having hairy leaves, often used in herbal medicine *(7)*

3   An early botanist *(9)*

4   Try again with fresh seeds *(5)*

5   Growing business in research and development *(7)*

6   Inspirational garden of Kent *(12)*

9   Much colder *(5)*

10   Fantasy figures guarding the earth *(6,6)*

15 Thick rhizomes of this common herb develop a violet scent when dried *(9)*

17 A sort of baking *(5)*

18 A sharp and fragrant spice is made from the dried fruit of this tropical American myrtaceous tree *(7)*

19 Information display *(7)*

20 Rousing country game *(7)*

22 Cloudy weather *(2,3)*

JUMBO CROSSWORD 41

ACROSS

1 Look out over a small garden *(6,3)*

8 18th-century garden setting for the King and Queen's fairy-tale honeymoon in Sleepy Doc Lane *(8,5)*

11 Flattened by wind and rain *(4)*

12 Races across the grounds *(5)*

13 Aromatic seedlike fruit used in medicine and for flavouring pickles *(4)*

16 Old World English roses are renowned for being . . . scented *(7)*

17 Cutting comment *(7)*

18 Genus of the acanthus family *(7)*

20 Tomato variety for the non-professional grower *(7)*

21 Chisel-like tool removes bark in chips, perhaps? *(4)*

22 Long-billed wading bird brings babies? *(5)*

23 Blister *(4)*

26 Fred Astaire played the title role in this film about a crane fly *(5-4-4)*

27 Old World spring-flowering plants *(9)*

DOWN

2 A date with destiny on 15th March *(4)*

3 Unlikely to put down roots *(7)*

4 Speculates curiously about the lettuce variety *(7)*

5 Elliptical field attracts cricket families *(4)*

6 Requests to borrow valued garden tools should, ideally, be met with this *(6,7)*

7 Ladies gate, etc. *(anag. 8,5)*

9 Pink variety of England's national emblem *(5-4)*

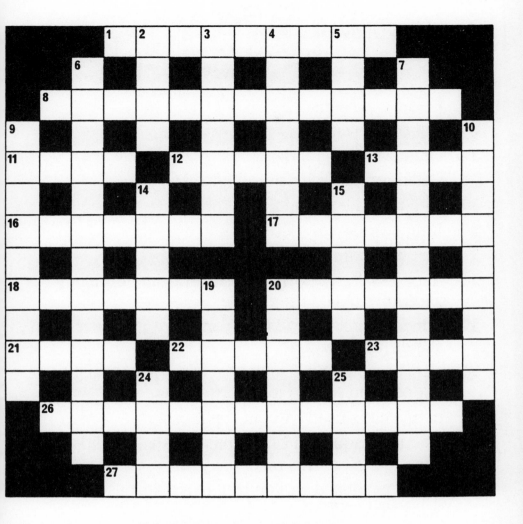

10 Varieties of *Prunus domestica* (4,5)

14 Plant stem (5)

15 Tobacco pipe made out of its root (5)

19 Genus of perennial plants of the family Saxifragaceae has clusters of red or white flowers (7)

20 Display the flowers nicely (7)

24 Sounds like a lazy god (4)

25 Twelfth month of the Jewish civil year (4)

JUMBO CROSSWORD 42

ACROSS

1 Leisure gardens *(10)*

6 Cut off by water *(4)*

10 Genus abbreviation *(7)*

11 Stinkhorn fungi are noted for this *(7)*

12 Genus of the graceful Columbine *(9)*

13 Rough track *(5)*

14 You'd be penniless without one *(1,4)*

15 Accounts for the origin of existing species from ancestors unlike them *(9)*

17 Punch-drunk field workers employed while the sun shines *(9)*

20 Leaf of the polygonaceous genus *Rumex* has this effect when rubbed into nettle stings *(5)*

21 In Spain it's plain without the trees *(5)*

23 Trafalgar Square's Christmas tree has traditionally been the gift of this race *(9)*

25 Crops produced without the use of fertilisers or pesticides *(7)*

26 The mistral blow *(3,4)*

27 Daylight display stand for indoor plants *(4)*

28 Consultant to the gardening stars? *(10)*

DOWN

1 Eaglewood of the genus *Aquilaria* is also known as this *(5)*

2 Done without haste *(9)*

3 Quantity of sherry for the fruit and custard dessert *(8,6)*

4 Pastoral poem *(7)*

5 High wind and root in a spin *(7)*

7 Feather grass genus *(5)*

8 Australian and American name for aubergines *(9)*

9 British landscape gardener noted for her simplicity of design and use of indigenous plants *(8,6)*

14 Plants without leaves *(9)*

16 Creative influence has a ring about it *(9)*

18 Attendants in no man's land *(7)*

19 Sounds like the gate needs oiling *(7)*

22 Grail made out of potters clay *(5)*

24 Bottom of the drain *(5)*

JUMBO CROSSWORD 43

ACROSS

1 Bill is delightful in the garden *(5, 7)*

7 Horny callosity at the foot of the tree? *(5)*

8 Sense of touch *(7)*

11 Spicy-scented hybrid derived from *Rosa odorata* *(3,4)*

12 Thrown out *(7)*

13 Field activity *(5)*

14 Annual balsaminaceous plant seems somewhat intolerant *(9)*

16 Plant of the heath family shares its name with a northern constellation between Cassiopeia and Pegasus *(9)*

19 Exemplary specimen *(5)*

21 Living on or near the surface of the open sea *(7)*

23 Professional pinnacle *(7)*

24 Everlasting *(7)*

25 Short-sleeved linen garment *(5)*

26 Scorzonera roots *(5,7)*

DOWN

1 Edible coarse seaweed of the genus *Laminaria* *(3-4)*

2 Efficient management of resources and avoidance of waste *(7)*

3 Unusual orange smuggled in through the Argentine *(9)*

4 Fibre obtained from the *Yucca* genus *(5)*

5 Generally acknowledged to be the most popular kind of *Hydrangea* *(7)*

6 *Anona*, a tropical genus of dicotyledons, includes this edible fruit *(7-5)*

9 Free from restraint *(5)*

10 Common name for the *Cypripedium calceolus* orchid *(5, 7)*

15 Concerned with hands-on experience *(9)*

17 Dig around *(5)*

18 Grown without the use of chemicals *(7)*

19 Masters of the arts *(7)*

20 Aromatic herb of the marjoram genus (*Origanum*), used in cookery *(7)*

22 Structural units of plants *(5)*

JUMBO CROSSWORD 44

ACROSS

1 Ajoining the flower beds *(9)*

8 . . . a lovesome thing, God wot *(7,6)*

11 A burden to carry *(4)*

12 Low, poorly drained land *(5)*

13 Figure cut from an apple of the West Indian Sapotaceous tree, *Chrysophyllum cainito* *(4)*

16 Time for the garden *(7)*

17 Pamphlet on foliage development *(7)*

18 Part of root vegetable above ground *(7)*

20 Bunch of fragrant flowers *(7)*

21 Leave it out *(4)*

22 Displayed blossom *(5)*

23 Sandy region *(4)*

26 Strong ties weathered fifty years *(6,7)*

27 Lubricant obtained from *Ricinus communis* *(6,3)*

DOWN

2 Nocturnal birds of prey *(4)*

3 Plant infection *(7)*

4 Immature, unconsolidated soil on which climate and vegetation have had little influence *(7)*

5 Designated standard *(4)*

6 Ultimate destination for one growing cannabis *(3,2,2,6)*

7 Abundantly productive land *(7,6)*

9 Could cost the earth, by all accounts *(9)*

10 Quite large, colloquially *(6,3)*

14 Widely cultivated garden plant, grown for its imposing racemes of pea-like flowers *(5)*

15 Effeminate fellow, colloquially *(5)*

19 Abnormal vegetable growth on plants *(7)*

20 Fresh start for the annuals *(3,4)*

24 Inspiration *(4)*

25 Pruning tried out by the Central Drug Research Institute *(4)*

JUMBO CROSSWORD 45

<u>ACROSS</u>

1   Eavesdrop, colloquially *(6)*

5   Helps prevent an increase in soil-borne pests and diseases *(8)*

9   Edible roots of the *Pastinaca sativa* plants *(8)*

10   Nearly finished and the cotton is cleared of seeds *(6)*

11   Hidden from view *(8)*

12   Plant of the marsh-mallow and hollyhock genus *(6)*

13   Lovable wild pansy takes root amongst the linseeds *(8)*

15   Concept *(4)*

17   Big reductions by the International Garden Centre Association *(4)*

19   Damaged plant turns out to be a grim load of *Calendula (8)*

20   Steps in the making *(6)*

21   Creature comfort sacrificed by landscape designer *(4,4)*

22   Opening passages *(6)*

23   Lemon-scented liquid from citronella grass *(8)*

24   Cape jasmine genus has built-in drainage *(8)*

25   Short-lived plectopterous insect *(6)*

<u>DOWN</u>

2   Spider *(8)*

3   Magnificent climbing shrub *(8)*

4   Genus of coarse, yellow-flowered asteraceous herbs. Dried leaves and tops of some are used in medicine *(9)*

5   Homes and gardens *(11,4)*

6 Cellular ring *(7)*

7 Lively dance *(5,3)*

8 Newly sown lawn comes into this category *(2-2,4)*

14 Worm's snot blown out in the fall *(9)*

15 When a young man's fancy lightly turns to thoughts of love *(2,6)*

16 Instructor *(8)*

17 Assign to a species *(8)*

18 Timothy grass *(4-4)*

19 Ground cover *(7)*

JUMBO CROSSWORD 46

ACROSS

1 Industrious individual digs in *(4,2,4)*
6 Aromatic fragrance *(4)*
10 Inclined to sink without water *(7)*
11 Plant-sucking insects make a feast of it *(7)*
12 Mineral matter formed by inward growth *(9)*
13 Get down to weeding *(5)*
14 Epidermal pore in plant leaves *(5)*
15 Top dressing for the winter *(9)*
17 Final attempt to improve drainage *(4,5)*
20 Common name for the *Populus alba* *(5)*
21 Hazel may help to find water *(5)*
23 Health hazard if it contains foul water *(4,5)*
25 Tidy and methodical *(7)*
26 Pulling strain *(7)*
27 Fun with a high flyer *(4)*
28 Popular term for the *Antirrhinum* *(10)*

DOWN

1 Adjustable shade adds a new dimension to the gloomy place *(5)*
2 Generic term for potatoes, beets, carrots and turnips *(4,5)*
3 Fruit on the stairs *(6,3,5)*
4 Celebration with flowers *(7)*
5 The language of flowers *(7)*
7 Herbaceous plant yielding aromatic seed *(5)*
8 Christmas decoration used symbolically at Druid sacrifices *(9)*

9 A growing business *(6,8)*

14 Dish of uncooked green plants or other vegetables served cold *(5,4)*

16 Doing this periodically in winter keeps powered implements in good condition *(9)*

18 Well-worn path *(7)*

19 Grounds for leaving – if it's the dregs *(7)*

22 Long-legged bird attracted to fish ponds *(5)*

24 Semi-transparent silk *(5)*

JUMBO CROSSWORD 47

ACROSS

1 Fruit of the eggplant *(9)*

8 Garden antiseptic and disinfectant *(4,9)*

11 A big race around the trees *(4)*

12 Tree produces cocoa butter *(5)*

13 Plant fluids come out of the ears *(4)*

16 Describes the corolla of plants such as the snapdragon *(7)*

17 Chinese-American dish of egg dough, filled with minced pork, bamboo shoots, onions, etc. *(3,4)*

18 Reproductive glands *(7)*

20 Perennial herb with white or pink flowers has a medicinal root used as a sedative *(7)*

21 The refuse of grapes after the juice has been extracted, used as a filter in making vinegar *(4)*

22 Wasteland overgrown with shrubs *(5)*

23 The largest continent *(4)*

26 Labour-saving implement *(10,3)*

27 Rat's heart still beating about the bushes *(9)*

DOWN

2 Unattractive vegetable growth *(4)*

3 Preparation contains plant juice *(7)*

4 May contain material worth composting *(7)*

5 Line caught in the river *(4)*

6 Bramley's are acknowleged to be the best variety of these *(7,6)*

7 Insect bites? Nudes risk none! *(5,4,4)*

9 Fruit of the baobab tree *(4,5)*

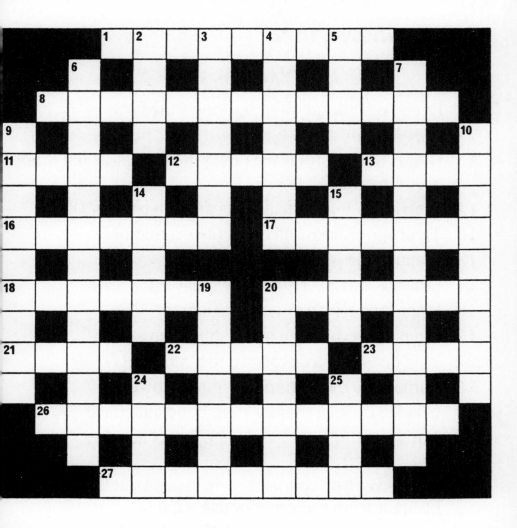

10 Canadian emblem *(5,4)*

14 Lukewarm *(5)*

15 Nimble *(5)*

19 Oily seed of the African sapotaceous tree, *Butyrospermum parkii* used as a food and in soap manufacture *(4,3)*

20 Infestations *(7)*

24 South American bird crossed with a rabbit *(4)*

25 Turned back the leaf to find a bloodsucker *(4)*

JUMBO CROSSWORD 48

ACROSS

1 Poetic encouragement to bring May flowers *(5, 7)*

7 Cereal killer *(5)*

8 Genus of toadstools including the fly agaric and other poisonous kinds *(7)*

11 District under the pastoral care of a bishop *(7)*

12 To propose (may fall on fertile ground) *(7)*

13 Manure the plot *(5)*

14 Disease carrier *(9)*

16 Plant food with a vegetarian starter *(9)*

19 Culinary herb of the mint family Labiate *(5)*

21 Wild ones could devastate the garden *(7)*

23 Camellia is this American state's flower *(7)*

24 Goaded by an irritating, one-eyed individual *(7)*

25 Native of the city once famed for its hanging gardens *(5)*

26 Glass-covered room into which plants in bloom are brought from the greenhouse *(12)*

DOWN

1 Genus of the windflower *(7)*

2 It always helps to say it with flowers *(7)*

3 No training required to use this. Simply pick it up as you go along *(6,3)*

4 Pile up the peas to keep in shape *(5)*

5 Grasses related to the bamboos *(7)*

6 Genus comprises evergreen and deciduous shrubs and trees with pink, purple or white flowers *(12)*

9 Ancient Celtic tribe led by Queen Boadicea *(5)*

10 Seasonal hazard on the roads *(6,6)*

15 Coffee-growing region *(5,4)*

17 Laid with food for the birds *(5)*

18 Tapering mass of frozen water *(7)*

19 Extreme hunger may induce this display by wild, albeit timid creatures *(7)*

20 Hasten the sprouting of hard covered seeds by abrasion *(7)*

22 Perspiration *(5)*

ACROSS

1   Perfume prepared from the flower of the red jasmine, *Plumeria ruba* *(10)*

6   Windmill vane *(4)*

10 Garlic bulbs *(7)*

11 Not so densely packed *(7)*

12 Composes lyrical poetry *(9)*

13 Celery's succulent bit covered in earth *(5)*

14 Perennial grass used for hay and pasture *(5)*

15 Pinaceous tree with leaves whitish beneath, *Abies alba*, widely planted for ornament *(6,3)*

17 Sensitivities to pollens, fruits, etc. *(9)*

20 Musical palindrome *(5)*

21 Low trees or shrubs, collectively *(5)*

23 Beet-stained fingers *(9)*

25 Consultant *(7)*

26 New variety of heather discovered in the USA *(7)*

27 Sort of species *(4)*

28 Common butterfly, *Vanessa atalanta* *(3,7)*

DOWN

1   Plants without true flowers and seeds *(5)*

2   Lubricant discovered in old loam *(6,3)*

3   Prickly shrub of the genus *Ribes grossularia* produces acid, globular fruit *(10,4)*

4   Makes a picture with its soft shades *(7)*

5   Organically grown *(7)*

7   Common name for *Lawsonia inermis* whose leaves are used to make a reddish orange dye *(5)*

8 Insecticide prepared from the dried heads of the composite genus *Chrysanthemum roseum* (9)

9 Law sitting associated with the wild aster (10,4)

14 Jack's ladder (9)

16 Money-grubber (9)

18 Inward growth (7)

19 Rosaceous genus popularly known as meadowsweet (7)

22 Raucous-voiced bird of ill-omen (5)

24 Drag or trail the plough (5)

JUMBO CROSSWORD 50

ACROSS

1 Succulent young shoots *(9)*

8 Oxeye daisy genus *(13)*

11 Trust it to make money grow *(4)*

12 Much above the usual size *(5)*

13 Fencing equipment *(4)*

16 Genus of perennial, epiphytic cacti with short jointed stems, each swollen at one end like a bottle *(7)*

17 Cabbage variety responds well to the cut-and-come-again treatment *(7)*

18 Down-to-earth individual *(7)*

20 Made to stand in the garden without clothes on in the coldest weather *(7)*

21 Jot or tittle *(4)*

22 Routine seed sowing method *(5)*

23 Bristle-like appendage in plants *(4)*

26 Another name for the autumn crocus *(6, 7)*

27 Tarragon, parsley, shallots, peppercorns and mustard are used for this excellent French butter sauce *(9)*

DOWN

2 Leguminous plant seeds used for food and livestock feed, and also yields a versatile oil *(4)*

3 Genus of evergreen climbers, often with scandent stems, grown for their flowers *(7)*

4 Ultra-violet rays which produce chemical changes *(7)*

5 Gorse genus *(4)*

6 Decorated conifer *(9, 4)*

7 Regal pelargonium *(6, 7)*

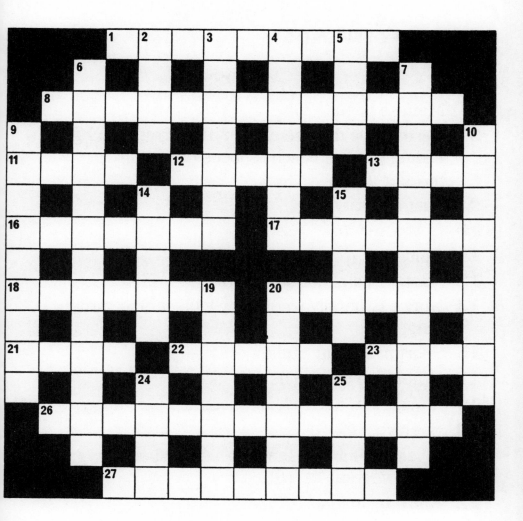

9 Botanical name for spurge *(9)*

10 Plant with a life cycle lasting more than two years *(9)*

14 Low truck or trolley *(5)*

15 Poisonous black spider *(5)*

19 Surname of influential gardener who enthused *Blue Peter* viewers *(7)*

20 Seedless raisin *(7)*

24 Advance gradually to the border *(4)*

25 Unidentified flies, facetiously *(4)*

ACROSS

1   Mimosa genus *(6)*

5   Cereal crop disease caused by a parasitic fungus, *Ustilago nuda*, which reduces the grains to powder *(5-3)*

9   Past maturity *(8)*

10 Herbal tea *(6)*

11 Gulfweed *(8)*

12 Another name for borax *(6)*

13 Notice generally ignored by louts within garden range *(2,6)*

15 Short projecting stump *(4)*

17 Otherwise it could be eels *(4)*

19 Mountain range rich in timber and pasturage *(8)*

20 Beehives *(6)*

21 Acidic vitamin present in plants, especially citrus and green vegetables *(8)*

22 Know by instinct *(6)*

23 Unbeatable consequence of **25 Across** *(4,4)*

24 A systemic insecticide is particularly effective in controlling this pest *(8)*

25 Strip the land bare *(6)*

DOWN

2   Flavouring substance obtained from the tonka bean *(8)*

3   Noise suggests a need to replace the lawnmower *(8)*

4   Shy relative is a hard nut to crack *(4,5)*

5   Stemless herb with a raceme of drooping, bell-shaped white flowers *(4,2,3,6)*

6 Viscous secretion found over more than just miles *(7)*

7 Carbon *(8)*

8 Growth-inhibiting altitude *(4,4)*

14 Practised training *(9)*

15 Insect control method *(8)*

16 The basin is full of wormwood *(8)*

17 Another name for tarragon *(8)*

18 Early bird's breakfast movement *(8)*

19 Classical garden designed within a four-sided courtyard, usually limited to palms in arid conditions *(7)*

JUMBO CROSSWORD 52

<u>ACROSS</u>

1   Uncultivated fruit pickers *(4,3,3)*
6   Creeps up as a rule *(4)*
10 Spanish dances around the tree trunks *(7)*
11 Moss-resistant stones *(7)*
12 Analysis of plant problems *(4,5)*
13 The lowest point *(5)*
14 Free from pollution *(5)*
15 Homely mulch *(3,6)*
17 One who gets the butterflies *(9)*
20 Behaves sulkily *(5)*
21 Pastoral poem *(5)*
23 Common name for *Senecio cruentus*, a composite plant of the Canary Islands *(9)*
25 Taped us, unusually, with the latest developments in the palm house *(7)*
26 Electromagnetic layers in the earth's upper atmosphere *(7)*
27 Earthy sediment *(4)*
28 Hard, fine-grained yellow wood produced by this large perennial *(6,4)*

<u>DOWN</u>

1   Botanical term for a tree *(5)*
2   Open to everybody *(9)*
3   Popular house plants of the genus *Saintpaulia ionantha* *(7,7)*
4   Offend good taste *(7)*
5   Lemon-scented plant *(7)*
7   Mayfly larva *(5)*

8 Dwellings which are limited to grow-bags and window boxes *(4-5)*

9 King Charles spaniel shares its name with an apple tree variety *(8,6)*

14 Tropical fruits used as a vegetable as well as a condiment *(9)*

16 Steam-producing device used for fumigation *(9)*

18 Chisel-edged tooth *(7)*

19 Growing strain *(7)*

22 Wild cry inspired, perhaps, by a Swiss gardener who sat on a wasps' nest! *(5)*

24 To go rotten (egg) *(5)*

JUMBO CROSSWORD 53

ACROSS

1 Any plant of the genus *Urtica* (6)

5 Common name for *Calendula* (8)

9 Newsreel pictures of the spaghetti harvest fall into this category (3-5)

10 Cardboard container (6)

11 Tanning material obtained from acorns of the Levantine oak (8)

12 Regular feed (6)

13 New generation approaching maturity (8)

15 Charity garden party (4)

17 Requirement (4)

19 Found the mite name in the intervening period (8)

20 Dessert apples (6)

21 Fruits of the genus *Prunus* (8)

22 Hollow, elongated body (6)

23 Caught in the wire netting (8)

24 Flowers for a blue lady (3,5)

25 Sacred beetle (6)

DOWN

2 Styled with ingenious simplicity (8)

3 Best in the show (3,5)

4 Sweet briar (9)

5 Salad leaves (7,3,5)

6 Formal gardens with strong architectural and symmetrical designs (7)

7 Composite herb covered with stiff hairs of the genus *Picris* (8)

8 Tree-like *(8)*

14 Outer sheath of close-set cells *(9)*

15 Old World moth of the genus *Ino*, characterised by brilliant metallic-green wings *(8)*

16 Sensitive cell *(5,3)*

17 Golden rod is this American state's flower *(8)*

18 Short-lived genus *(8)*

19 Sour-cherry *(7)*

JUMBO CROSSWORD 54

ACROSS

1   Fungal growth on the main road, perhaps? *(5,4)*

8   Irascible personality *(7,6)*

11 Welcome cold shower *(4)*

12 Common name for the green plover *(5)*

13 Cry of a stag at rutting-time *(4)*

16 Prostrate stems throw out roots and shoots to produce new plants *(7)*

17 Little round beetle, brightly spotted, preys on aphids *(7)*

18 Fruits of the tree genus *Juglans regia* *(7)*

20 Botanical name for the tree of heaven *(7)*

21 Traditional knowledge of plants *(4)*

22 Thick hairy coating *(5)*

23 Variety of barley *(4)*

26 Production plants *(8,5)*

27 Waste reduction units *(9)*

DOWN

2   Upper and lower divisions of a flower corolla or calyx *(4)*

3   Kidney-shaped nuts *(7)*

4   Shadow clock *(7)*

5   Hardy cereal *(4)*

6   Preserves places of natural beauty *(8,5)*

7   A dab hand at gardening *(5-8)*

9   Sir Winston Churchill's home for forty years *(9)*

10 Former chairman of Gardeners' Question Time *(4,5)*

14 Classification of plants *(5)*

15 Full-grown *(5)*

19 Unshaven growth *(7)*

20 Arrangement on display *(7)*

24 Network *(4)*

25 Gate post *(4)*

JUMBO CROSSWORD 55

ACROSS

1 Raise funds with a gentle drive amongst the insects *(6)*

5 Aubergine *(8)*

9 Rodent family member *(8)*

10 Love apple *(6)*

11 Iris family members with sword-shaped leaves and spikes of bright flowers *(8)*

12 Afternoon nap induced by a tassie *(6)*

13 Arid song in the garden could invite a drenching *(4,4)*

15 Wire support *(4)*

17 Edgings *(4)*

19 Restore an old garden *(8)*

20 Active constituent of creosote *(6)*

21 Pleasant change now that darkness is no more *(8)*

22 Shared interests *(6)*

23 There is no chemical control for such rings on lawns *(2,6)*

24 Narcotic alkaloid contained in opium *(8)*

25 Male crawlers *(3,3)*

DOWN

2 Gum tree *(8)*

3 Unsettled weather *(8)*

4 Cut short *(9)*

5 Common name for the genus *Oenothera* *(7,8)*

6 Showy blooms concealed in one's pie *(7)*

7 Water, colloquially *(5,3)*

8 Gardening gloves for extra hands *(3,5)*

14 Harmless insect of the order *Odonata* (9)

15 Typical example (8)

16 Toothless mammal eats termites (8)

17 Red ones taken up the garden path (8)

18 Soft drink for the suckers (8)

19 Plant support system (7)

JUMBO CROSSWORD 56

ACROSS

1 Warm ocean current drifts towards the British Isles *(4,6)*

6 Old *(4)*

10 Colourless acid with a fruity taste, found in some plants and used in synthetic resins *(7)*

11 Long-lasting fruits *(7)*

12 Join the growing attraction *(9)*

13 Reap with a sickle *(5)*

14 Cooked and sieved vegetables or fruit *(5)*

15 Verdict on the cannabis field trial *(3,6)*

17 Coated with egg-white *(9)*

20 Using arson really plumbs the depths! *(5)*

21 Bird of prey throws in the towel *(5)*

23 Ornamental garden lighting *(4,5)*

25 Homes and gardens buried here by Vesuvius *(7)*

26 Landscape as pretty as a picture *(4,3)*

27 Irish river flows across the border *(4)*

28 Give an honest and helpful opinion *(6,4)*

DOWN

1 Terms of reference for the European Group of National Pesticide Manufacturers' Associations *(5)*

2 Brown seaweed genus *(9)*

3 Common name for *Arbutus unedo* *(10,4)*

4 Starting pistol *(4,3)*

5 European plant of the borage family whose root yields a red dye *(7)*

7 Land attached to a parish church *(5)*

8 Pest control official, facetiously *(9)*

9 14th-century mansion and gardens near Tunbridge Wells, Kent; birthplace of the poet, Sir Philip Sidney *(9,5)*

14 Country cooking *(6,3)*

16 Painting of greater width than depth *(9)*

18 The guacharo *(7)*

19 Military retainer of a Japanese feudal noble, holding land or a stipend in rice *(7)*

22 Unsaleable car, colloquially *(5)*

24 Bristle-like appendage *(5)*

JUMBO CROSSWORD 57

ACROSS

1 Seeds used in flavouring bread, also yield an edible oil *(6)*

5 Pigeons home in on paper bags *(8)*

9 Plant pore *(8)*

10 Weaken in strength *(6)*

11 Common name for the genus *Asperula* which bears sweet-scented white flowers and fragrant leaves used to flavour wine *(8)*

12 Ringed game for the table *(6)*

13 Well-earned rest *(3,5)*

15 Clippings ordered by the American Society of Newspaper Editors *(4)*

17 British Society of Dowsers concentrates on a small grassy area *(4)*

19 Unspoilt natural environment *(8)*

20 Widespread protest if anything happened to ruin **19 Across** *(6)*

21 Gallinaceous bird makes short work of the ant heaps *(8)*

22 Geese, collectively *(6)*

23 Characteristic of one who is well versed *(8)*

24 Condition of one who could have been through a hedge backwards *(8)*

25 Expect them to run in the garden *(6)*

DOWN

2 Neglected gardens *(8)*

3 Remedy for a tetanoid condition *(8)*

4 Have a word with the plants *(9)*

5 Papavaraceous herb of North America's Pacific coast, with showy yellow flowers *(10,5)*

6 Stone boundary of a sandy alluvial deposit *(7)*

7 Specimens *(8)*

8 Saw-edge leaf *(8)*

14 Incredulity *(9)*

15 Weather-ruined crops *(3,2,3)*

16 Savings out of clutches *(4,4)*

17 Filmy crust formed on wine after long keeping *(8)*

18 Surface excavation *(8)*

19 One who takes a running jump *(7)*

JUMBO CROSSWORD 58

ACROSS

1 Strange wader discovered amongst the aquatic life *(5,7)*

7 Bloodsucking flies *(5)*

8 German measles brought about by playing with the pressurised spray *(7)*

11 Physical and chemical conditions of the soil in relation to the plant and animal life it supports *(7)*

12 Bottom of the heap *(4,3)*

13 Rapeseed *(5)*

14 Citrus fruit seed *(6,3)*

16 Reptiles kept as domestic pets *(9)*

19 Soup or stew, containing chicken, thickened with okra pods *(5)*

21 Irritating flea bite *(7)*

23 More than two or three, but not many more *(7)*

24 Trial excavation *(7)*

25 Genus of the true firs *(5)*

26 Alcoholic solution of a vegetable drug *(5,7)*

DOWN

1 Small Old World bird of the family *Motacillidae* *(7)*

2 Air-conveying tube in insects and other arthropods *(7)*

3 So our case is full of five petalled flowers *(9)*

4 Apple stuck in the throat *(5)*

5 Swift movements *(7)*

6 Heralds of spring *(5,7)*

9 Fruit juice, boiled with sugar *(5)*

10 Cultivated grass out of condition *(4,8)*

15 Hopefully, another hand with ten green fingers *(9)*

17 Toxic protein derived from castor oil seeds used in experimental cancer therapy *(5)*

18 Japanese art of folding paper to make flowers *(7)*

19 Chile hazel nut genus *(7)*

20 Heavier crop of tomatoes *(4,3)*

22 Diving bird of the order *Colymbiformes* *(5)*

JUMBO CROSSWORD 59

ACROSS

1 Small active bug of the order *Heteroptera*, feeds on plants, causing damage to crops *(6)*

5 Rudimentary *(8)*

9 Back and forth *(2,3,3)*

10 Dependent *(6)*

11 Palmy coastal resorts *(8)*

12 Strong prepared solution *(6)*

13 Agave fibre used for making ropes *(8)*

15 Sooty fungal disease of flowering plants *(4)*

17 Taken by mouth *(4)*

19 Peak period for poinsettia sales *(8)*

20 Flowering time for meadow saffron *(6)*

21 Child's analogy for mole runs *(3,5)*

22 Prayer *(6)*

23 Nine in number *(8)*

24 Faces the rising sun *(4,4)*

25 South American crocodilian, similar to the alligator *(6)*

DOWN

2 Genus of plants with poisonous or medicinal properties, such as monkshood or wolfsbane *(8)*

3 Natural source of ultra-violet radiation *(8)*

4 Respect *(9)*

5 Spring pick-me-up for acid-hating plants *(4,11)*

6 Builder specialised in walled borders *(7)*

7 Needle-shaped *(8)*

8 Out of doors *(8)*

14 Early stage of development *(9)*

15 Maple tree *(8)*

16 Apples and pears above the ground floor *(8)*

17 Common-or-garden *(8)*

18 Candied stems used in cookery *(8)*

19 Dark-blue fruits of *Prunus institia* *(7)*

JUMBO CROSSWORD 60

ACROSS

1 Bill and Ben *(9,3)*

7 Travelling bags used to smuggle a sprouting shrub *(5)*

8 Refreshment facility for visitors to public gardens *(7)*

11 Energy of motion applied to lifting *(7)*

12 Raised mass of earth *(7)*

13 Specific job to be done *(5)*

14 Thistle-like Eurasian plant, *Cynara scolymus*, cultivated for its large edible flower head *(9)*

16 Uniform colour *(5,4)*

19 Exhausted *(5)*

21 Finished up in shallow water in Durango *(7)*

23 Cotton fabric *(7)*

24 Experienced gardener has a few wrinkles up his sleeve *(3,4)*

25 Bit of a liberty having to prove one was somewhere else *(5)*

26 Recipes for a popular variety of gooseberry *(8,4)*

DOWN

1 Stubs *(3,4)*

2 Sedative drugs *(7)*

3 Place of rest *(4,5)*

4 Small plot for cabbages *(5)*

5 Contains the toxic rodent and insect poison *(7)*

6 Baked spud *(6,6)*

9 Convex moulding also known as a quarter round *(5)*

10 Home grown produce also helps one's ability to dot this *(4,4,4)*

15 Vehicles for the slippery slopes *(9)*

17 Colourful characters noticed on unstable land *(2,3)*

18 Follow examples of good practice *(7)*

19 Wrens, colloquially *(7)*

20 Genus of herbaceous perennials having showy flowers and tuberous roots *(7)*

22 Duck! *(5)*

JUMBO CROSSWORD

SOLUTION 1

ACROSS

1 Gazebo
5 Cabbages
9 Lager can
10 School
11 Camellia
12 Design
13 Tartness
15 Cats
17 Base
19 Hairbell
20 Cloudy
21 Hardcore
22 Storax
23 Utilised
24 Styptics
25 Tweeds

DOWN

2 Anabaena
3 Elements
4 Oscularia
5 Container shrubs
6 Buckets
7 Gloxinia
8 Selenite
14 Spearmint
15 Crocuses
16 Taxonomy
17 Black ice
18 Sharp end
19 Hydrant

SOLUTION 2

ACROSS

1 Angustifolia
7 Mop up
8 Break in
11 Oarweed
12 Disdain
13 Salts
14 Log cabins
16 Aggregate
19 Chomp
21 Dentate
23 Nervate
24 Roseate
25 Excel
26 Infestations

DOWN

1 Admiral
2 Gophers
3 Sapodilla
4 Imbed
5 Oversea
6 Jacob's ladder
9 Khaki
10 None-so-pretty
15 Green belt
17 Genus
18 Exarate
19 Curaçao
20 Oracles
22 Erect

SOLUTION 3

ACROSS

1 Tomato
5 Bird's-eye
9 Key asset
10 Septic
11 Shanghai
12 Dinars
13 Abutting
15 Elul
17 Legs
19 Nepenthe
20 Hoeing
21 Existing
22 Sit-ups
23 Flinched
24 Serenity
25 Ensure

DOWN

2 Overhaul
3 An annual
4 Oasthouse
5 Bats in the bel
6 Dieting
7 Entrance
8 Excesses
14 Nutritive
15 Emphasis
16 Unfetter
17 Lettuces
18 Grandeur
19 Ninepin

UMBO CROSSWORD

SOLUTION 4

CROSS

Pimpernel
Coming up roses
1 OPMA
2 Devil
3 Menu
6 Ascarid
7 Secrete
8 Impress
0 Agamete
1 Tips
2 Flora
3 Star
6 Depth of winter
7 Breadroot

OWN

Iris
Pigweed
Repairs
Eros
Too much pepper
Severe weather
Botanists
0 Juneberry
4 Gruel
5 Scrap
9 Salsola
0 A grower
4 Stir
5 Undo

SOLUTION 5

ACROSS

1 Spades
5 Clematis
9 Freeze-up
10 Extine
11 Sub-shrub
12 Addict
13 Onyx lump
15 ISAW
17 ADFA
19 Stetsons
20 League
21 Bistoury
22 Noises
23 Oxidised
24 Seedsmen
25 Exhume

DOWN

2 Perfumes
3 Deep snow
4 Swear by it
5 Capability Brown
6 Mixed up
7 Trinidad
8 Sweetpea
14 Moonshine
15 Inclines
16 Alkaline
17 Astonish
18 Fair Geum
19 Saucers

SOLUTION 6

ACROSS

1 Bramble jelly
7 Sable
8 Reposed
11 Breathe
12 Tureens
13 Oasis
14 Peasouper
16 Hit and run
19 Corgi
21 Oilrigs
23 Parasol
24 Succour
25 Roost
26 Caribbean Sea

DOWN

1 Bushels
2 Arbutus
3 Beekeeper
4 Egret
5 Esparto
6 Bamboo shoots
9 Steep
10 Desert island
15 Annapurna
17 Telic
18 Nairobi
19 Cordons
20 Rosetta
22 Shrub

JUMBO CROSSWORD

SOLUTION 7

ACROSS

1   Secateurs
8   Pineapple weed
11   Oast
12   Robot
13   Plan
16   Dampest
17   Mindful
18   Reeking
20   Beeches
21   Mess
22   Forum
23   Info
26   Hanging garden
27   Gipsy moth

DOWN

2   Eden
3   Asprout
4   Eelworm
5   Rows
6   Midsummer's day
7   Peal of thunder
9   Cold frame
10   In blossom
14   Leg it
15   Inter
19   Grounds
20   Blue gum
24   Ugli
25   Grit

SOLUTION 8

ACROSS

1   Broad beans
6   Song
10   Incurve
11   Teheran
12   Saintfoin
13   Enate
14   Beefy
15   Eradicate
17   Eyebright
20   Gloom
21   Known
23   Anteaters
26   Mophead
27   So-so
28   Use the loam

DOWN

1   Bliss
2   Orchideae
3 & 25 Across
    Dorothy Frances Gurney's
4   Eyesore
5   Notanda
7   Ocrea
8   Gynaeceum
9   Thieving magpie
14   Breakages
16   Above zero
18   Grasses
19   To tempt
22   Orris
24   Sedum

SOLUTION 9

ACROSS

1   Acotyledon
6   Acid
10   The buds
11   Turnips
12   High grade
13   Imago
14   Grown
15   Eradicate
17   Sunstroke
20   Itchy
21   Aspen
23   Umbellate
25   Inspect
26   Arouser
27   Nest
28   Panellists

DOWN

1   Aitch
2   Overgrown
3   Young and tender
4   Ensnare
5   Ootheca
7   China
8   Discovery
9   Artificial pool
14   Gestation
16   Archaisms
18   Opuntia
19   Embrace
22   Pests
24   Earls

SOLUTION 10

CROSS

	Pineapple
	Kitchen garden
1	Frog
2	Dijon
3	Mini
6	Seeding
7	Suffuse
8	October
0	Gradual
1	Ties
2	Spend
3	Et al
6	Silver birches
7	Crispness

OWN

	Itch
	Evening
	Pigeons
	Lore
	Dig one's toes in
	Deciduous tree
	Offshoots
0	Tiger lily
4	Limbs
5	Offal
9	Reports
0	Gentian
4	Over
5	Aces

SOLUTION 11

ACROSS

1	Thermometers
7	Nails
8	Sapient
11	Norwich
12	Shortie
13	Eclat
14	Popinjays
16	Fragrance
19	Attar
21	Ill wind
23	Satiate
24	Subsoil
25	Noise
26	Top dressings

DOWN

1	Tendril
2	Elitist
3	Misshapen
4	Mists
5	Typhoon
6	Thunderflies
9	Extra
10	Tree surgeons
15	Pheasants
17	Ad lib
18	Rhizoid
19	Antlion
20	Teasels
22	Delve

SOLUTION 12

ACROSS

1	Asafoetida
6	Mats
10	Pigweed
11	Spinose
12	Nerviness
13	Tenet
14	Adobe
15	Tudor rose
17	Chamomile
20	Lanes
21	Eaten
23	Lie in wait
25	Incense
26	Thin air
27	Sash
28	Astragalus

DOWN

1	Aspen
2	Algarroba
3	One fine morning
4	Tidiest
5	Disused
7	Adorn
8	Scentless
9	Winter planting
14	Asclepias
16	Of no avail
18	Illness
19	Elector
22	Ticks
24	Taros

JUMBO CROSSWORD

SOLUTION 13

ACROSS

1 Digitalis
8 Horticultural
11 AFMA
12 Smear
13 Mint
16 Pansies
17 Parsnip
18 Niagara
20 Society
21 Logs
22 Slope
23 Mere
26 Walter Raleigh
27 Fred Loads

DOWN

2 Iota
3 Incomes
4 All damp
5 IFUW
6 Norman Vaughan
7 Radiant energy
9 Campanula
10 Staphylea
14 Lilac
15 Erica
19 Allured
20 Sapsago
24 Stir
25 Feed

SOLUTION 14

ACROSS

1 Spring onions
7 Rosin
8 Lifting
11 Paprika
12 Dirtier
13 Older
14 Evaporate
16 Amaryllis
19 Sward
21 Infused
23 Heavens
24 Gullies
25 Table
26 Bloodsuckers

DOWN

1 Scraped
2 Rustier
3 Nonpareil
4 Oiled
5 Inferno
6 Crop rotating
9 Ibiza
10 Garden design
15 Aesthetic
17 Awful
18 Yoshino
19 Scabble
20 Ageless
22 Doses

SOLUTION 15

ACROSS

1 Orchid
5 Acanthus
9 Kohlrabi
10 Hempen
11 Gentiana
12 Clutch
13 Programs
15 Bats
17 Pane
19 As a poker
20 Remark
21 Lenticel
22 Whinny
23 Ethiopia
24 Regiment
25 Yields

DOWN

2 Rhodesia
3 Hilltops
4 Diana Dors
5 Animal repelle
6 Needles
7 Hepatica
8 Sunshade
14 Making hay
15 Borrower
16 Tramping
17 Pruinose
18 Nice wind
19 Acronym

SOLUTION 16

ACROSS

Malathion
8 Hedge trimmers
11 Undo
12 Nelis
13 Echo
16 Kennels
17 Goggles
18 Ermined
20 Scissor
21 Okra
22 Abort
23 CSFE
26 Carpet beetles
27 Prisoners

DOWN

Alga
Anthers
Hailing
OHMS
Bedding mortar
Trickle system
Muskmelon
10 Moss-green
14 Jeans
15 Again
19 Debates
20 Surgeon
24 Spur
25 Stir

SOLUTION 17

ACROSS

1 Small bulbs
6 Mesh
10 Arrowed
11 Upright
12 Typifying
13 Sorgo
14 Vetch
15 Gardeners
17 Ball joint
20 Irons
21 Ripen
23 Herculean
25 Ungular
26 In a seed
27 Soya
28 At the altar

DOWN

1 Scant
2 Acropetal
3 Law of the jungle
4 Undoing
5 Blunger
7 Eiger
8 Hothouses
9 *Iris reticulata*
14 Viburnums
16 Elopement
18 Inherit
19 Tarnish
22 Pigmy
24 Nadir

SOLUTION 18

ACROSS

1 Afternoon
8 Irish moss peat
11 Rays
12 Betel
13 Idea
16 Send off
17 Tetanus
18 Mimulus
20 Pacific
21 Tuna
22 Tawny
23 Geum
26 Nitrate of soda
27 Andromeda

DOWN

2 Fish
3 Elm leaf
4 Nascent
5 OAPs
6 Praying mantis
7 Landing fields
9 Grass moth
10 Capsicums
14 Holly
15 Stack
19 Scatter
20 Pinworm
24 Bran
25 Used

JUMBO CROSSWORD

SOLUTION 19

ACROSS

1 Sage and onion
7 Tulip
8 Titania
11 Biocide
12 Soakage
13 Tines
14 Accretion
16 Aesthetic
19 Stump
21 Roadman
23 Liqueur
24 Nigeria
25 Amour
26 Primrose path

DOWN

1 Sit down
2 Gullies
3 Apple-cart
4 Dates
5 Nitrate
6 Rabbit warren
9 NAAFI
10 Awe-inspiring
15 Cochleate
17 Slang
18 Humdrum
19 Sequoia
20 Unearth
22 Ngaio

SOLUTION 20

ACROSS

1 Trowel
5 Hammocks
9 Coolibar
10 Floral
11 Allodial
12 Raisin
13 Thousand
15 Uses
17 Tsar
19 As a flash
20 Estate
21 Price tag
22 Dipper
23 In a chain
24 Dragging
25 Sorrel

DOWN

2 Rootless
3 Wild oats
4 Lubricous
5 Heralds of spring
6 Mallard
7 Cerastes
8 Silencer
14 No animals
15 Unseeded
16 Earth pea
17 Thresher
18 Alkaline
19 Ant's egg

SOLUTION 21

ACROSS

1 Titchmarsh
6 Corm
10 Ripened
11 Clarkia
12 Arabinose
13 Bands
14 Cling
15 Sterilise
17 Cutlasses
20 Graft
21 Mound
23 Varieties
25 Eternal
26 Catmint
27 Sods
28 Bed of roses

DOWN

1 Terra
2 Topiarist
3 Hanging garden
4 Arduous
5 Secrete
7 Oaken
8 Mead-sweet
9 Rambling recto
14 Cucumbers
16 Inanities
18 Seville
19 Sirocco
22 Upend
24 Sites

UMBO CROSSWORD

SOLUTION 22

ACROSS

Little gem
Contemplation
1 Rule
2 Stipe
3 Itch
6 Singled
7 Exclaim
8 Mistral
0 Trophic
1 Show
2 Cumin
3 Ital
6 Weather-beaten
7 Eggshells

DOWN

Iota
Tempted
Eclipse
Eats
Rolling stones
Toothache tree
Irish moss
0 Chemicals
4 Flare
5 Scion
9 Laurels
0 Thimble
4 Stag
5 Fall

SOLUTION 23

ACROSS

1 Background
6 Plum
10 Scarlet
11 Grubbed
12 Lookalike
13 Urali
14 Chili
15 Extensive
17 Clever dog
20 Aries
21 Shrew
23 Ground ash
25 Ontario
26 Tropics
27 Bane
28 Belladonna

DOWN

1 Basil
2 Chamomile
3 Galvanised wire
4 Outsize
5 Neglect
7 Libra
8 Muddiness
9 Autumn lawn
food
14 Cockscomb
16 Imitation
18 Dog rose
19 Glottal
22 Ratan
24 Hosta

SOLUTION 24

ACROSS

1 Pelargoniums
7 Lit up
8 Look out
11 Spatial
12 Proviso
13 Oxeye
14 Elevation
16 Fingertip
19 Brash
21 Uniform
23 Rhubarb
24 Toddies
25 Under
26 Hedge sparrow

DOWN

1 Peltate
2 Lattice
3 Repellent
4 Oxlip
5 Ipomoea
6 Passionfruit
9 Oribi
10 Two in the bush
15 Empyreuma
17 Naiad
18 Eroding
19 Boulder
20 A barrow
22 Mists

JUMBO CROSSWORD

SOLUTION 25

ACROSS

1 Coral spot
8 Passionflower
11 Hawk
12 Diary
13 Guru
16 Netting
17 Needful
18 Circles
20 Decayed
21 Axle
22 Agate
23 Frau
26 Asparagus tips
27 Onion skin

DOWN

2 Oust
3 Atoning
4 Saffron
5 Oboe
6 Eat with relish
7 Venus flytraps
9 China clay
10 Pulled out
14 Field
15 Fence
19 Saguaro
20 Detours
24 Dawn
25 RTPI

SOLUTION 26

ACROSS

1 Backwaters
6 Gale
10 Avignon
11 Nearest
12 Sagebrush
13 Green
14 Spike
15 Essential
17 Same kinds
20 Bided
21 Awash
23 Wolfsbane
25 Overdue
26 Quested
27 Noah
28 Great start

DOWN

1 Beaks
2 Clingfilm
3 Windbreak shade
4 Tonsure
5 Ranches
7 Abele
8 Entangled
9 Hanging baskets
14 Saskatoon
16 Indian tea
18 New Year
19 Siliqua
22 Areca
24 End it

SOLUTION 27

ACROSS

1 Garlic
5 Foxglove
9 Golf club
10 Hazard
11 Parlance
12 Digger
13 Stifling
15 Aces
17 Sybo
19 Bedstraw
20 Redbud
21 Paeonies
22 Sparse
23 Olibanum
24 Open days
25 Spells

DOWN

2 Aromatic
3 Lifeless
4 Celandine
5 Fibreglass pool
6 Glazing
7 Orangery
8 Eldorado
14 Nurseries
15 Alfresco
16 Eradiate
17 Swan Lake
18 Bisexual
19 Bruised

UMBO CROSSWORD

OLUTION 28

CROSS

September
Almond blossom
1 Item
2 Rotor
3 Baby
6 Icicles
7 Slender
8 Tighter
0 Also-ran
1 Reed
2 Afire
3 Knee
6 Fresh as a daisy
7 Cranberry

OWN

Ebon
Tedious
Mallows
Ease
Bleeding heart
Total darkness
Miniature
0 Hydrangea
4 Gluts
5 Geest
9 Refrain
0 Acreage
4 User
5 Pair

SOLUTION 29

ACROSS

1 Witch hazel
6 Hall
10 Lateral
11 Pruning
12 Sump hoses
13 Fruit
14 Spoil
15 Soda water
17 Emergence
20 Épées
21 Laser
23 Conundrum
25 Nowhere
26 Big idea
27 Sods
28 Green trees

DOWN

1 Wells
2 Totem pole
3 Hare Hill Garden
4 Atlases
5 Exposed
7 Adieu
8 Ligatures
9 Guy Fawkes night
14 Seedlings
16 The bridge
18 Nuclear
19 Ennoble
22 Sawed
24 Meals

SOLUTION 30

ACROSS

1 Papaya
5 Growbags
9 Dinosaur
10 El Giza
11 Latinise
12 Tureen
13 Eustomas
15 Lair
17 Salt
19 Esterase
20 Pretty
21 Gossamer
22 Reefer
23 Annually
24 Gathered
25 Ageing

DOWN

2 Avifauna
3 Atomiser
4 Acariasis
5 Garden of
    England
6 Walnuts
7 Aliceara
8 Stagnant
14 Adansonia
15 Leapfrog
16 Interest
17 Separate
18 Luteolin
19 Extreme

JUMBO CROSSWORD

SOLUTION 31

ACROSS

1 Euphorbia
8 Bougainvillea
11 East
12 Shave
13 Acer
16 Brogues
17 Lumbago
18 Endives
20 Residue
21 Seta
22 Braes
23 Tutu
26 In the trenches
27 Cash crops

DOWN

2 Urge
3 Heights
4 Revival
5 Ills
6 Cotswold stone
7 Peace and quiet
9 Redbreast
10 Arboretum
14 Guava
15 Smash
19 Scratch
20 Roe deer
24 Thea
25 ICBP

SOLUTION 32

ACROSS

1 Dried blood
6 BFPC
10 Ambling
11 Thunder
12 Elongated
13 Indra
14 Lasso
15 Recreated
17 Campanula
20 Biter
21 Elder
23 Susurrant
25 Orcinol
26 Naivety
27 Dusk
28 Enthusiast

DOWN

1 Dwale
2 In blossom
3 Dying for a drink
4 Lighter
5 Octadic
7 Faded
8 Coriander
9 Juniper berries
14 Lichenoid
16 Tetranema
18 Upsilon
19 Absinth
22 Docks
24 Try it

SOLUTION 33

ACROSS

1 Aaron's rod
8 Royal Hospital
11 Soho
12 Caked
13 Geum
16 Trumpet
17 Shudder
18 Enemies
20 Caldron
21 Lily
22 Fibre
23 SAFU
26 On bended kne
27 Pixy stool

DOWN

2 Adam
3 Oxheart
4 Sisters
5 Ohio
6 Hothouse plan
7 Lavender wate
9 Tsetse fly
10 Amarantus
14 Aphid
15 Curly
19 Spindly
20 Cured it
24 Yeti
25 INTO

OLUTION 34

CROSS

	Carrot
	Bergamot
	Wisteria
0	Badger
1	Dovetail
2	Mimosa
3	Tricycle
5	Isis
7	Oats
9	Amnesiac
0	Enigma
1	Doggerel
2	Static
3	Isotopes
4	Dressing
5	Nosing

OWN

	Amitosis
	Retreats
	Terrarium
	Bramley seedling
	Granite
	Magnolia
	Terraces
4	Lying down
5	Immersed
6	Irrigate
7	Ocherous
8	Tree fern
9	Armpits

SOLUTION 35

ACROSS

1	Tree of heaven
7	Erica
8	Situate
11	Elating
12	Eyebrow
13	Fates
14	Agropyron
16	Underfeed
19	Fichu
21	Moisten
23	Epigyny
24	Rosella
25	Pride
26	A vase of roses

DOWN

1 & 6	The last rose of summer
2	Elixirs
3	Orangeade
4	Haste
5	Antwerp
9	Airer
10	Edwin Lutyens
15	Red pepper
17	Drips
18	Rattles
19	Fairies
20	Clypeus
22	Ngaio

SOLUTION 36

ACROSS

1	Bird colony
6	Soap
10	Endemic
11	Melilot
12	Surrounds
13	Congo
14	Beano
15	Scavenger
17	Integrate
20	Elemi
21	Spoor
23	Ever since
25	Oilwell
26	In stars
27	Espy
28	Dragonhead

DOWN

1	Beets
2	Redbreast
3	Common-or-garden
4	Lychnis
5	Nemesia
7	Orlon
8	Potpourri
9	Black-eyed Susan
14	Brimstone
16	Greengage
18	Areolar
19	Evening
22	Oxlip
24	Eased

JUMBO CROSSWORD

SOLUTION 37

ACROSS

1   Camass
5   Gladioli
9   Deer-hair
10 Inkcap
11 Rusty hoe
12 Azalea
13 Nitrogen
15 Sang
17 Eyes
19 Cinnamon
20 Faeces
21 Minerals
22 Inulin
23 No hearts
24 Soapsuds
25 Lahore

DOWN

2   Arequipa
3   Aerating
4   Spaghetti
5   Garden
    ornaments
6   Denizen
7   Oscology
8   Implants
14 Emmenthal
15 Sawflies
16 Nubecula
17 Encroach
18 Emulator
19 Clerics

SOLUTION 38

ACROSS

1 & 28 *Helleborus
        orientalis*
6   Hops
10 Malacca
11 Produce
12 Drainpipe
13 Bread
14 Clear
15 Non-edible
17 Drenching
20 Extol
21 Roast
23 Stiff ones
25 Raw deal
26 Paunchy
27 Etna

DOWN

1   Humid
2   Liliaceae
3   Eccentricities
4   Ovation
5   Umpteen
7   Ovule
8   Speedwell
9   Forbidden fruit
14 Cedar tree
16 Botanical
18 Insular
19 Glimpse
22 Aswan
24 Soyas

SOLUTION 39

ACROSS

1   Chickweed
8   Dig for victory
11 Odds
12 Awake
13 Avon
16 Nunnery
17 Epaulet
18 No heart
20 Pioneer
21 Echo
22 Divot
23 Asps
26 Under Milk W◄
27 Claremont

DOWN

2   Haft
3   Caraway
4   Wrinkle
5   EFTA
6   Bird in the han◄
7   Travellers' joy
9   John Innes
10 Knotgrass
14 Relax
15 Razor
19 Trimmer
20 Problem
24 Tell
25 Twin

JMBO CROSSWORD

SOLUTION 40

CROSS

Jack Harkness
Comer
Sorting
Siberia
Weedier
Nanny
Ivory-tree
Herb Peter
Debug
Roadmen
Saguaro
Tetanus
Outré
Bed of nettles

OWN

Jacobin
Comfrey
Herbalist
Resow
Nursery
Sissinghurst
Icier
Garden gnomes
Orrisroot
Roast
Pimento
Digital
Beaters
No sun

SOLUTION 41

ACROSS

1 Window box
8 Polesden Lacey
11 Laid
12 Acres
13 Dill
16 Sweetly
17 Sarcasm
18 Rhellia
20 Amateur
21 Spud
22 Stork
23 Stye
26 Daddy-Long-Legs
27 Bluebells

DOWN

2 Ides
3 Didicoy
4 Wonders
5 Oval
6 Polite refusal
7 Delicate stage
9 Blush-rose
10 Plum trees
14 Stalk
15 Briar
19 Astilbe
20 Arrange
24 Idol
25 Elul

SOLUTION 42

ACROSS

1 Allotments
6 Isle
10 Initial
11 Reeking
12 Aquilegia
13 Trail
14 A bean
15 Evolution
17 Haymakers
20 Eases
21 Llano
23 Norwegian
25 Organic
26 Dry wind
27 Sill
28 Astrologer

DOWN

1 Agila
2 Leisurely
3 Trifling amount
4 Eclogue
5 Tornado
7 Stipa
8 Eggplants
9 Gertrude Jekyll
14 Aphyllous
16 Inspiring
18 Eunuchs
19 Stridor
22 Argil
24 Nadir

JUMBO CROSSWORD

SOLUTION 43

ACROSS

1   Sweet William
7   Acorn
8   Tactual
11 Tea rose
12 Ejected
13 Rugby
14 Impatiens
16 Andromeda
19 Model
21 Pelagic
23 Treetop
24 Eternal
25 Cotta
26 Black salsify

DOWN

1   Sea-tang
2   Economy
3   Tangerine
4   Istle
5   Laciest
6   Custard-apple
9   Untie
10 Lady's slipper
15 Practical
17 Delve
18 Organic
19 Maestri
20 Dittany
22 Cells

SOLUTION 44

ACROSS

1   Bordering
8   English garden
11 Onus
12 Marsh
13 Star
16 Leisure
17 Leaflet
18 Topping
20 Nosegay
21 Omit
22 Blown
23 Gobi
26 Golden wedding
27 Castor oil

DOWN

2   Owls
3   Disease
4   Regosol
5   Norm
6   End up in prison
7   Fertile ground
9   Pollution
10 Pretty big
14 Lupin
15 Pansy
19 Gallnut
20 New Year
24 Idea
25 CDRI

SOLUTION 45

ACROSS

1   Earwig
5   Rotation
9   Parsnips
10 Ending
11 Shielded
12 Althea
13 Idleness
15 Idea
17 IGCA
19 Marigold
20 Pacing
21 Lost nest
22 Intros
23 Rhodinal
24 Gardenia
25 Mayfly

DOWN

2   Arachnid
3   Wisteria
4   Grindelia
5   Residential ar
6   Annulus
7   Irish jig
8   No-go area
14 Snowstorm
15 In spring
16 Educator
17 Identify
18 Cat's-tail
19 Manhole

JMBO CROSSWORD

OLUTION 46

CROSS

- Hard at work
- Balm
-) Drooped
- 1 Mealies
- 2 Secretion
- 3 Kneel
- 4 Stoma
- 5 Greatcoat
- 7 Last ditch
-) Abele
- 1 Dowse
- 3 Open drain
- 5 Ordered
- 5 Tension
- 7 Lark
- 3 Snapdragon

OWN

- Hades
- Root crops
- Apples and pears
- Wedding
- Romance
- Anise
- Mistletoe
- Market gardener
- 4 Salad bowl
- 5 Operating
- 3 Trodden
-) Heeltap
- 2 Wader
- 4 Ninon

SOLUTION 47

ACROSS

- 1 Aubergine
- 8 Soil sterilant
- 11 Oaks
- 12 Cacao
- 13 Sera
- 16 Ringent
- 17 Egg roll
- 18 Ovaries
- 20 Allheal
- 21 Rape
- 22 Heath
- 23 Asia
- 26 Mechanical aid
- 27 Earthstar

DOWN

- 2 Ugli
- 3 Extract
- 4 Garbage
- 5 Nile
- 6 Cooking apples
- 7 Under one's skin
- 9 Sour gourd
- 10 Maple leaf
- 14 Tepid
- 15 Agile
- 19 Shea nut
- 20 Attacks
- 24 Rhea
- 25 Flea

SOLUTION 48

ACROSS

- 1 April showers
- 7 Ergot
- 8 Amanita
- 11 Diocese
- 12 Suggest
- 13 Dress
- 14 Bacterium
- 16 Nutrients
- 19 Basil
- 21 Rabbits
- 23 Alabama
- 24 Needled
- 25 Iraqi
- 26 Conservatory

DOWN

- 1 Anemone
- 2 Regrets
- 3 Litter bin
- 4 Heaps
- 5 Whangee
- 6 Rhododendron
- 9 Iceni
- 10 Autumn leaves
- 15 Costa Rica
- 17 Table
- 18 Icicles
- 19 Bravado
- 20 Scarify
- 22 Sudor

JUMBO CROSSWORD

SOLUTION 49

ACROSS

1 Frangipani
6 Whip
10 Ramsons
11 Thinner
12 Sonneteer
13 Heart
14 Brome
15 Silver fir
17 Allergies
20 Minim
21 Scrub
23 Crimsoned
25 Adviser
26 America
27 Kind
28 Red admiral

DOWN

1 Ferns
2 Almond oil
3 Gooseberry bush
4 Pastels
5 Natural
7 Henna
8 Pyrethrum
9 Michaelmas term
14 Beanstalk
16 Financier
18 Incurve
19 Spiraea
22 Raven
24 Drail

SOLUTION 50

ACROSS

1 Asparagus
8 Chrysanthemum
11 Unit
12 Giant
13 Épée
16 Hatiora
17 Chinese
18 Realist
20 Snowman
21 Iota
22 Drill
23 Seta
26 Meadow saffron
27 Béarnaise

DOWN

2 Soya
3 Asarina
4 Actinic
5 Ulex
6 Christmas tree
7 Purple emperor
9 Euphorbia
10 Perennial
14 Bogie
15 Widow
19 Thrower
20 Sultana
24 Edge
25 UFOs

SOLUTION 51

ACROSS

1 Acacia
5 Loose-cut
9 Autumnal
10 Tisane
11 Sargasso
12 Tincal
13 No litter
15 Snag
17 Else
19 Pyrenees
20 Apiary
21 Ascorbic
22 Intuit
23 Less game
24 Greenfly
25 Denude

DOWN

2 Coumarin
3 Chugging
4 Aunt Sally
5 Lily of the vall
6 Slimier
7 Charcoal
8 Tree line
14 Exercised
15 Spraying
16 Absinthe
17 Estragon
18 Squirmed
19 Persian

SOLUTION 52

CROSS

	Adam and Eve
	Inch
0	Boleros
1	Rolling
2	Root cause
3	Nadir
4	Clean
5	Tea leaves
7	Pessimist
)	Mopes
1	Idyll
3	Cineraria
5	Updates
5	Ionised
7	Silt
3	Orange tree

OWN

	Arbor
	Allcomers
	African violets
	Disgust
	Verbena
	Naiad
	High-rises
	Blenheim orange
4	Capsicums
5	Vaporiser
3	Incisor
)	Tension
2	Yodel
4	Addle

SOLUTION 53

ACROSS

1	Nettle
5	Marigold
9	Leg-pulls
10	Carton
11	Vallonia
12	Dinner
13	Children
15	Fete
17	Need
19	Meantime
20	Eaters
21	Cherries
22	Tubule
23	Enmeshed
24	Red roses
25	Scarab

DOWN

2	Elegance
3	Top place
4	Eglantine
5	Mustard and cress
6	Italian
7	Oxtongue
8	Dendroid
14	Epidermis
15	Forester
16	Taste bud
17	Nebraska
18	Ephemera
19	Morello

SOLUTION 54

ACROSS

1	Black spot
8	Waspish nature
11	Hail
12	Pewit
13	Bell
16	Runners
17	Ladyfly
18	Walnuts
20	Ailanto
21	Lore
22	Furry
23	Bere
26	Assembly lines
27	Shredders

DOWN

2	Lips
3	Cashews
4	Sundial
5	Oats
6	National Trust
7	Green-fingered
9	Chartwell
10	Clay Jones
14	Genus
15	Adult
19	Stubble
20	Arrayed
24	Mesh
25	Pier

JUMBO CROSSWORD

SOLUTION 55

ACROSS

1 Beetle
5 Eggplant
9 Sciurine
10 Tomato
11 Gladioli
12 Siesta
13 Rain gods
15 Stay
17 Hems
19 Recreate
20 Cresol
21 Moonrise
22 Mutual
23 Of fungus
24 Narceine
25 Yes men

DOWN

2 Eucalypt
3 Thundery
4 Epitomise
5 Evening
   primrose
6 Peonies
7 Adam's ale
8 Two pairs
14 Dragonfly
15 Specimen
16 Anteater
17 Herrings
18 Moisture
19 Rootage

SOLUTION 56

ACROSS

1 Gulf stream
6 Aged
10 Fumaric
11 Keepers
12 Bandwagon
13 Shear
14 Puree
15 Not guilty
17 Glaireous
20 Sonar
21 Owlet
23 Lamp posts
25 Pompeii
26 Real art
27 Erne
28 Advise well

DOWN

1 GEFAB
2 Laminaria
3 Strawberry tree
4 Race gun
5 Alkanet
7 Glebe
8 Destroyer
9 Penshurst Place
14 Pigeon pie
16 Landscape
18 Oilbird
19 Samurai
22 Lemon
24 Setal

SOLUTION 57

ACROSS

1 Sesame
5 Carriers
9 Lenticel
10 Impair
11 Woodruff
12 Hoopla
13 Tea break
15 ASNE
17 BSOD
19 Heritage
20 Outcry
21 Pheasant
22 Gaggle
23 Poetical
24 Disarray
25 Tights

DOWN

2 Eyesores
3 Antidote
4 Encourage
5 California pop
6 Rimrock
7 Examples
8 Serrated
14 Amazement
15 Act of God
16 Nest eggs
17 Beeswing
18 Opencast
19 Hurdler

JMBO CROSSWORD

OLUTION 58

CROSS

Water gardens
Gnats
Aerosol
1 Edaphic
2 Skid row
3 Colza
4 Orange pip
5 Tortoises
9 Gumbo
1 Itching
3 Several
4 Sondage
5 Abies
6 Fluid extract

OWN

Wagtail
Trachea
Rosaceous
Adam's
Darting
Hazel catkins
Syrup
0 Lawn problems
5 Assistant
7 Ricin
8 Origami
9 Gevuina
0 More set
2 Grebe

SOLUTION 59

ACROSS

1 Capsid
5 Inchoate
9 To and fro
10 Addict
11 Rivieras
12 Liquor
13 Henequen
15 Smut
17 Oral
19 December
20 Autumn
21 Toy mines
22 Orison
23 Enneadic
24 East side
25 Cayman

DOWN

2 Aconitum
3 Sunlight
4 Deference
5 Iron sequestrene
6 Hadrian
7 Acicular
8 External
14 Embryonic
15 Sycamore
16 Upstairs
17 Ordinary
18 Angelica
19 Damsons

SOLUTION 60

ACROSS

1 Flowerpot men
7 Grips
8 Tearoom
11 Kinetic
12 Hillock
13 Tasks
14 Artichoke
16 Olive drab
19 Jaded
21 Aground
23 Gingham
24 Old hand
25 Alibi
26 Careless uses

DOWN

1 Fag ends
2 Opiates
3 Easy chair
4 Patch
5 Thallic
6 Jacket potato
9 Ovolo
10 Make ends meet
15 Toboggans
17 In red
18 Emulate
19 Jennies
20 Dahlias
22 Dodge